FINALLY...AFTE[R]

THE RAREST

MOST DESIRABLE

MOST SOUGHT AFTER

MOST VALUABLE

PREMIUM....

IN THE HISTORY OF THE WORLD
IS NOW AVAILABLE AGAIN

FOR THE FIRST TIME EVER...

Davy Crockett Figure
1950s, $60

**Dennis The Menace
(Dennis)**, 1960s, $40

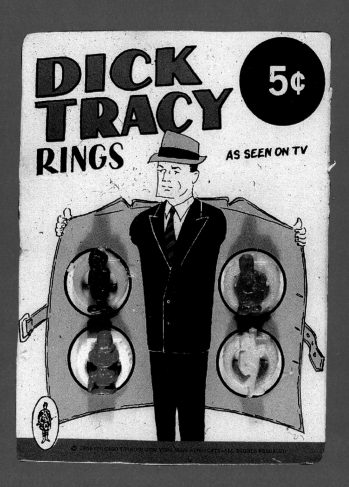

**Dick Tracy Card
with 4 character rings**, 1966, $150 complete

Dick Tracy Hat
1930s, $400

Dizzy Dean
1936, $175

Doctor Doolittle Flicker
1970s, $60

Dick Tracy Monogram
1930s, $1600

Dick Tracy Secret Compartment
1940s, $500

Felix The Cat Flicker (blue base)
(set of 3), 1960s, $30

Fonz
1970s, $125

Frankenberry Flicker
1980s, $75

Frank Buck Black Leopard
1938 (silver version), $1800

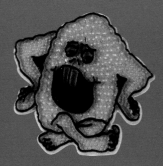

Freakies Figural
1978, $100

Frank Buck Ivory Initial
1940s, $350

Garfield Flicker
(set of 3), 1978, $10

Gene Autry Flag
1950s, $200

Hopalong Cassidy Bar 20
1950s, $60

Golden Nugget Cave
1950s, $500

Howdy Doody Clarabelle Flicker
1950s (set of 8), $30

Green Hornet Secret Compartment
1947, $1200

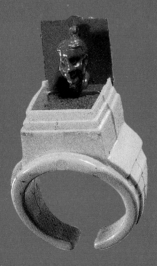

Howdy Doody Jack In The Box
1950s (rare color variant), $5200

ZORRO ™

ie GREAT AMERICAN RING
.UB INC. is proud to intro-
ıce another quality col-
ectible character ring.
:aturing the Classic rearing
ırse on the face, this beauti-
l precious metal ring is sure
ɔ be a treasured collectible.
ıblazoned on each side of
ıe shank is the Mark of
rro...the mark that gives

vailable in Sterling Silver or 10k Gold in small, medium, and large, it is pack-
ɟed in a leather satchel w/drawstring also marked with the famous "Z". This
lition is extremely limited and is sure to be an investment that will increase
ı value for years to come. Sterling Silver is limited to only 500 pieces, 10k
ɔld to an edition of 100. Don't miss your opportunity to own the Zorro

GRADING

The more valuable the ring the more important accurate grading becomes. A ring in MINT condition is worth more than in GOOD condition and the value difference could be considerable. Rings should be graded with a keen eye for detail and close attention should be given to luster, surface wear and defects, color chipping and fading, damage, plastic altered by heat, plating wear, missing parts, replaced parts and restoration before a grade is assigned. The following grades should be used to more accurately describe the condition of your rings.

MINT (MT): Same condition as issued; complete with full luster and no sign of wear. Rarely occurs in 1930s to 1940s rings. In very rare cases, rings have occurred with unbent prongs on otherwise fitted rings and are worth a premium. Rings in this condition could bring considerably more than the Near Mint (NM) listing.

NEAR MINT (NM): Nearly perfect with the slightest evidence of wear and 90% luster to the naked eye. Generally the highest grade reached by most of the metal rings.

VERY FINE (VF): Wear beginning to show on high points, but 70% of the surface shows luster. Very minor color flaking may be evident but the overall appearance is still very desirable.

FINE (FN): Still enough luster to be desirable. General wear beginning to show. Less than 70% and more than 50% luster evident. Slightly above average condition.

VERY GOOD (VG): Most of the luster is gone, general wear, tarnishing and fading is the general rule. Prongs can be bent but are still complete. On plated rings, base metal can be seen over much of the ring. Paper (where applicable) could be stained but is still legible and complete. Most rings that have been cleaned will fall into this grade.

GOOD (GD): Below average condition. Still complete but prongs can be chipped or bent, color or plating will be gone. Surface abrasion and wear is obvious but all parts must be present.

FAIR (FR): Excessive wear obvious. A minor part may be missing.

POOR (PR): Incomplete and not suited for investment purposes.

HISTORY

From the beginning of time man has been fascinated and intrigued with the mystique of rings. Before the discipline of science, during the middle ages and beyond, in a world of sorcerers, wizards and witches, some believed that rings exists that possess special powers over man.

Boris Karloff used a ring to bring down his victims in the famous 1933 movie "The Mummy." Carl Barks picked up on the idea and wrote his first complete story "The Mummy's Ring" (Four Color #29, 1943) which was a smash hit to comic book collectors. A red ring played a major role in the recent 1994 film "The Shadow." In baseball collecting, the Pennant and World Series rings are highly prized and are on collectors' want lists. Price guides exist on antique rings of a generic nature and are quite popular. It only seems reasonable that our industry should have a guide on comic related rings, both premiums and store bought.

Beginning in the 1930s the premium ring was an early device given away to children to trace consumer response to various products. The producers were quick to use words like "mysterious, mystic, scarab, lucky, cosmic, ancient, dragon, Egyptian, Aztec, secret, magical," etc. reinforcing this ancient belief that rings truly do possess magical and secret properties.

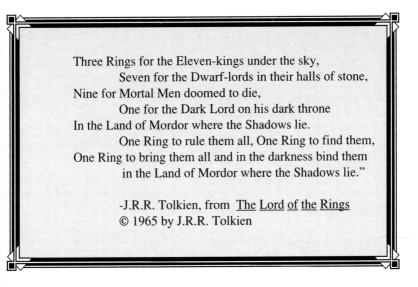

Three Rings for the Eleven-kings under the sky,
    Seven for the Dwarf-lords in their halls of stone,
Nine for Mortal Men doomed to die,
    One for the Dark Lord on his dark throne
In the Land of Mordor where the Shadows lie.
    One Ring to rule them all, One Ring to find them,
One Ring to bring them all and in the darkness bind them
    in the Land of Mordor where the Shadows lie."

-J.R.R. Tolkien, from The Lord of the Rings
© 1965 by J.R.R. Tolkien

Cereal companies, sponsors of radio and television shows, beverage com panies, food producers, movie studios, comic book companies, toy producers sports promoters, etc. gave away many different types of premiums including rings to survey what type of products their customers were buying. At the same time, the first comic books and Big Little Books began to appear.

The earliest premium ring is the **Lone Wolf Tribal**, made of sterling sil ver, which was offered in 1932 by Wrigley Gum (the sponsor of a popular radio show) to test listener response. Soon after this historic first, the famous comic strip character Little Orphan Annie got her own nationally broadcast radio show. Now known as "Radio" Orphan Annie, dozens of premiums began appearing on the market, including some of the rarest rings ever offered any where. The ROA Altascope (only 6 known) was the last ring offered before the radio show was canceled and is the rarest of the ROA rings. The ROA magni fying and initial rings are the next most difficult ROA rings to find. Other popular characters' rings from the 1930s included Buck Rogers, Tom Mix, Frank Buck and Melvin Purvis. The Tom Mix Deputy ring from 1935 was very difficult to acquire and today is one of the 10 rarest rings.

Box tops, candy or gum wrappers, coupons, etc. were required in most cases to receive the premium. The radio adver tisers believed that the amount of response each product received was an indicator of its acceptance level. The response could even be used as regional indicators by offering certain premiums exclu sively to certain geographic areas. Some rings were only offered in a small area while others, like the Kix Atom Bomb, exploded all over the country.

> The earliest premium ring is the **Lone Wolf Tribal**, a 1932 Wrigley Gum giveaway made of sterling silver.

The earliest rings were made of metal and usually exhibited excellent qual ity in design and material (some were even gold plated) and are highly prized by collectors. Most of the early metal rings were made by the **Robbins Company**. In recent years there was a very exciting "archive find" of rings and ring parts from this company which included complete rings as well as a few one-of-a-kind prototypes and different ring bases only.

During the 1940s the sponsors of popular radio shows such as The Shadow, The Lone Ranger, Sky King, Green Hornet and Superman offered pre mium rings to listeners. The Lone Ranger Atom Bomb, also given away through Kix cereal in 1946, was the most successful premium ever with over million produced. Today this ring is still revered as one of the most beautiful and desirable because of its breathtaking design and eye-catching gold, silver and red colors.

The most valuable of these rings is the **Superman of America member ship ring** which was shipped to 1600 winners of the Action Comics contest in arly 1940. Only 10 complete examples of this ring are known to exist, with all but one in less than near mint condition.

The appearance of plastic in the late 1940s made it possible to produce rings at less cost. A few plastic rings began to appear as early as 1941 (Shadow Blue Coal) but did not get into full swing until the 1950s.

With the invention of television (a new concept of combining radio with movies) in the late 1940s, no one could have predicted the impact this new entertainment medium would have in such a short period of time. By 1950 the first television comic book, Howdy Doody, was published. Soon, many premiums were given away through popular television shows. The **Howdy Doody Jack in the Box ring** is the rarest plastic item from this era. Just as in radio, the premiums were used to test viewer response.

Western comic books jammed the stands in 1948 and science fiction comics began to appear in 1950. The most popular characters from the movies were marketed to the public in comic books, on radio and eventually on television. Gene Autry, Roy Rogers, Gabby Hayes, Hopalong Cassidy, Space Patrol, Captain Video and others had their rings too.

During the 1960s dozens of plastic rings of television show celebrities abounded. Addams Family, Dark Shadows, Beatles, Davy Crockett, Munsters, Tarzan, Batman are just a few. Cereal personalities such as Quisp and Quake also had their series of rings. In fact, the Quisp figural ring is the most valuable after 1959.

The 1970s saw rings from Star Wars (film), Star Trek (TV), McDonalds (hamburger chain), Huckleberry Hound (TV), Captain Crunch (cereal), etc.

Companies continued promoting their characters during the 1980s with G.I. Joe, Gumby, Marvel Comics character rings, Lucky Charms (cereal) and others. One of the most ambitious ring programs ever initiated was the 1990s Ring Raiders with an amazing 68 rings in the set!

Today, the comic book companies are producing high quality rings directly for the collectors market. Spawn by McFarlane, X-O, X-Men, Spiderman, Superman, Green Lantern, Teenage Mutant Turtles, G.I. Joe and Diamond Comic Distributors' promotional rings such as Batman, The Shadow, and X-Men.

Collecting rings is a fascinating challenge and many can be purchased at very moderate prices. Unlike some collectibles, rings are very easy to display because of their small size. If handled properly rings maintain their look and beauty with very little effort.

Price guides exist for antique rings of a generic nature and are quite popular. With the ground swell of interest in the collectibility of premium rings, it is only fitting that our hobby have a Price Guide and the "legitimacy" which it confers. The future of ring collecting looks bright as new collectors enter the market every day, and it's easy to see that the era of serious ring collecting is here!

USING THIS BOOK

This reference work is the most complete, accurate, and comprehensive listing and photographic index of collectible rings ever attempted. All listings are arranged alphabetically by the name of the character, event, type, style, company or subject. The listings are placed on each page <u>vertically</u> and should be referenced from top to bottom. It is our goal to eventually show an illustration for <u>every</u> listing.

Some of the scarcer and more interesting rings may have additional illustrations to show more detail. Boxed notations are also used to explain in greater detail the functions of particular rings. Before purchasing a ring, check the illustration and description in this book to be sure all the parts are included. Complete ring sets are listed <u>as sets</u> when known with a complete photographic reference where possible. The rings of a set are linked with arrows pointing down (usually located in the lower left corner of each illustration). The price is linked to the set above with an arrow pointing up. Rings missing from sets will be included whenever possible in future editions.

> If a ring is a logical candidate for cross referencing, it will be listed in more than one location.

Additional information includes dates as well as a description (if needed) and price range. Pay close attention to detail when comparing your ring with the illustrated example to make sure identification is accurate. Many rings appear similar and lack identifying markings making this reference the only way of correctly identifying certain rings. Take this book with you on all your ring buying trips.

If you have a ring that should be included in future editions, please send a detailed description with a photograph to the author.

> The advertisers in this book can often provide invaluable assisance to novice and advanced collector alike. Consider contacting them with your questions and wants.

STARTING A COLLECTION

Today the comic book companies are producing collectible rings based on our favorite logos and comic characters. These are available through most comic book stores or can be ordered via mail order catalogs (e.g. Warner Brothers, Disney, etc.). Most of these offerings are limited editions and sell out quickly, so be prepared to pay a premium price if you purchase them from dealers or collectors after production is discontinued. Of course the older rings are difficult to find. They can be bought from reliable dealers and at comic and collectible shows throughout the country.

Before starting your collection, consider studying the photographs in this guide to broaden your knowledge of the rings you may want to collect. Pay special attention to the details and visual subtleties of each ring. This is important because there are a few cases where older rings have been duplicated in recent times and are similar in design. The new rings are never exactly identical to the originals and usually look "brand new" in appearance.

Frequently collectors discover rings unknown to the market and not listed in this guide at toy shows, antique shows, premium shows, and comic book conventions. When these new discoveries are documented, they will be added to future editions of this book.

Many of the premium rings came with a mailing envelope or box and papers (referred to by collectors as instructions). Ring paper is usually scarce and is a very valuable and an interesting addition to any ring collection. Other rings appeared in groups attached to cards. When searching for rings at shows, don't forget to look for the larger card sets. They can sometimes be easy to overlook.

Rings were offered in cereal box promotions, newspaper comic section and comic book ads. These advertising pages make a ring collection display more colorful and interesting.

Most rings are still inexpensive and affordable to collectors. The market is young and new discoveries are always possible to the energetic searcher. Many of the rare rings lack identifying markings, making it possible to discover rare rings in unlikely places (flea market bargain bins and the like).

Your collection can be displayed in ring boxes and special ring display mounts available from jewelry suppliers.

RINGS OF THE FUTURE

Marvel Comics launched their ring program in 1994. The first of the series was the Xavier Class Ring. Sources there suggest that they plan to continue producing this ring each year for the graduating class from the Xavier Institute. For example, next year the ring will be changed to the "Class of 95". Each limited edition quantity would remain the same as in 1994: 250 10K Gold; 2,500 Sterling Silver & unlimited Bronze finished pewter. With the popularity of X-Men, these top quality rings should be highly prized by collectors.

X-Men Xavier ring by Marvel Ent. Group.

Marvel plans to expand this program into other X-Men affiliated schools which may be established in the future. Marvel is also considering developing character identifiable rings based on their more popular characters. So be on the look out for more collectible Marvel rings in the near future.

Tekno Comix trademark ring

Other comic book companies are planning to initiate ring programs as well.

DC has licensed the release of a version of the highly valued 1940s Superman prize ring. This ring will be produced in solid gold as well as other less expensive metals.

Tekno Comix also has plans of producing several rings. Their first ring is a heavy metal secret compartment issue (see illustration above) of excellent quality and eye appeal. Valiant Comics released their X-O ring in 1993 and are planning to produce more rings in the future. Watch out for Image and other comic companies who may be producing rings for their popular characters as well.

RINGS IN THIS GUIDE

This book contains over 2300 illustrations, which are individually described, dated and priced.

The following guidelines for ring listings in this reference work will apply. Rings are listed alphabetically by character, company, sets or type. Rings based on comic characters, celebrities, sports figures, movies, TV shows, fictional characters, etc. are included. All rings are made of metal, precious metal, plastic, paper, cardboard, etc. Most rings were offered as premiums by the sponsors of radio shows, TV shows, movies, cereals, candys, gums, etc. and are included. Other listed rings were sold to the public through ads in comic books, stores, mail offerings, catalogues, etc.

> Contains over 2300 illustrations, with individual descriptions and prices.

Another category of rings included are the new collectible rings being produced by distributors, comic book companies and others with the collector in mind.

All "paper" associated with each ring will be listed, illustrated and priced when available. Items associated with the advertising and promotion of certain rings may be included which could consist of ring cards, actual ads, headers for gumball machines or display promotional signs.

> All premium type rings, store rings and new rings of popular characters will be included in the listings.

Not included in this work are many of the generic gumball machine rings and general toy rings produced past and present. Basically, the criteria for inclusion of a ring is based primarily on collector demand and interest and historical importance. Please notify the author if you have rings not listed that should be included in future editions.

ABOUT RING PRICES

The prices in this guide are in U.S. currency and reflect the market jus prior to publication. These reported prices are based on (but not limit ed to) convention sales, dealers lists, stores, auctions and privat sales. The author invites sales lists, sales reports or any other infor mation pertaining to ring information or sales

PRICES IN THIS BOOK ARE FOR ITEMS IN GOOD AND NEAR MINT CONDITION

The values listed are for complete examples and represent **Good** and **Nea Mint** condition where only two prices are shown. The more valuable anc scarcer rings may have addition grades priced to reflect a wider spread in the value.

Other rings that generally turn up incomplete will be priced in this way with additional prices for the missing parts. Examples are: Rocket to the Moon ring came with 3 rockets. Prices are listed for the ring and also for the rockets The Captain Video Flying Saucer ring has prices for the base as well as the saucers which are usually missing. The Radio Orphan Annie triple mystery ring usually occurs with the top missing, so prices for the top and base are given.

When rings appear on cards or in sets, both the individual price and the se price may be given.

The values in this book are **retail prices**, not dealers' wholesale prices Dealers will pay a percentage of the listed prices when buying inventory and this percentage will vary from dealer to dealer. Some dealers are only interested in buying rings in strict near mint or mint condition, while others will buy in al grades.

FLICKER RINGS

by Howard Weinberger

Flicker rings and Flicker premiums began to emerge as the production of the high quality Golden Age premiums of the 1930s to 1950s began to fade. This new technology, a lenticular plastic laid over a specially photographed image, would catch anyone's eye. As you tilted a flicker piece back and forth, or side to side, like magic the image would either change completely to another image, or would continue the motion of the same image producing an animation effect. It was almost like watching a cartoon "move" right there on your finger!

Its appeal was not only limited to kids either. Flicker political buttons and rings were quite the rage from the late 1950s thru the 1960s. In fact, while the golden age premium rings were limited to the handful of characters that existed from the 1930s to the 1950s, flicker rings had no such limitations and covered everything! In addition to numerous random subjects (like the Civil War), flicker rings chronicled one of America's most revolutionary and pivotal times, the 1950s and 1960s. Politics, music, T.V. shows, radio, cartoons, current events, places, restaurants and a veritable plethora of products were all the subject of flicker rings. From JFK and Martin Luther King to the first man on the moon; from Elvis, the Beatles and the Monkees to Batman, Howdy Doody, Soupy Sales and Laugh-In; from McDonald's, Sears, Hush Puppies and Buster Brown to the 1964 Worlds Fair and Mister Softee – flicker rings covered it all!

The popularity of flicker rings has never faded either. New premiums continued to be produced through the 1970s and 1980s, and will likely continue well into the future.

Some of the earliest flickers we know of are the Howdy Doody and Davy Crockett T.V. flickers from the early 1950s. Also, there was the "thick lens" Rootie Kazootie and Howdy Doody Poll Parrot rings with a metal band that held the flicker onto the base with four prongs. The Buster Brown Club and "I like Mister Softee" were two other examples of very collectible early flicker rings.

Vari-Vue International became the dominant force in the market by producing rings from the late 1950s right through the 1960s. Vari-Vue revolutionized flicker rings by introducing hundreds of beautiful, brightly colored and highly detailed individual rings and ring sets. A few smaller manufacturers continued making rings as they still do today, but not with the same quality or quantity as Vari-Vue. Of the estimated 400-500 different individual flicker rings ever produced, Vari-Vue probably produced two-thirds of them.

Even though flicker rings are generally more readily available than most of the Golden Age premium rings, quite a few sets and individual rings are becoming increasingly more difficult to find, especially on their original or authentic ring bases.

THE PLASTIC RING BASE

A flicker is in Mint condition when the picture is centered and cut perfectly with no lines or images from other rings showing, and no cracks in the lenticular lens.

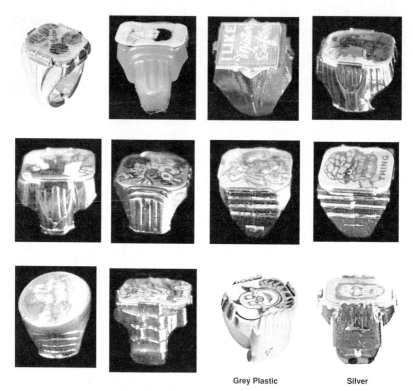

Grey Plastic   Silver

All above illustrations are examples of original ring bases.

FLICKER BASES FALL INTO 3 TYPES

1). Original plastic ring base. The original base as first distributed is the most desirable. There are a number of different styles. Both gold and silver plastic bases were originally issued. It is not unusual to find a particular set utilizing two or three different original ring bases. The significance of the original base proves that the ring was at some point actually in circulation. If the ring is Mint in an unopened package or has the original plastic base, it (at least) dates from the original issue, and was in a gumball machine, a package of cereal, or on a cardboard display for sale. These original pieces should carry a premium and have a higher value than any other examples.

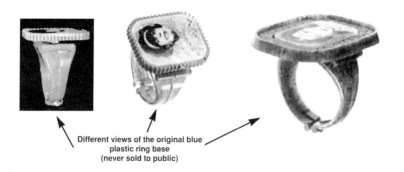

Different views of the original blue
plastic ring base
(never sold to public)

2). Blue-plastic wide-bordered ring base. These bases are the next type of ring. Although there are many stories regarding these rings, it is generally agreed that these bases are original Vari-Vue products. (This conclusion is based on countless discussions with collectors, dealers and people claiming to have been present at the Vari-Vue liquidation auctions.)

If you look on the back of many examples, you can find imprints of "Walt Disney Production." Some rings have this area stamped over, so it's not legible on every ring. My understanding is that these bases came into being because Vari-Vue and Disney were going to produce some type of Disney rings, but the deal never happened and no flickers were produced. However, Vari-Vue had produced thousands of blue plastic bases in anticipation of a deal.

These ring bases were then moth-balled in the Vari-Vue warehouse. When the Vari-Vue company went out of business, the warehouse inventories were auctioned off. Many caches of loose flicker pieces were found, as well as these empty blue ring bases. After the auction, some enterprizing dealers decided to attach the loose flickers into the blue bases, thus creating a new form of flicker ring. Even though the flicker pieces and the ring bases are indeed original, they were probably never assembled or distributed by the company.

Modern v-base produced in china

3). The modern ring base. The last variation, although it looks very nice, is really the least valuable. Within the last couple of years, cheap flicker rings were produced in China on silver based rings with a "V" on each side. There were a number of flicker images produced. They are poor quality with faded color and weak flicker action. The flicker piece is about twice as thick as an original Vari-Vue flicker piece.

Of these flickers, about five or so are direct "bootlegs" of the Looney Tune's flickers done by Vari-Vue. BEWARE. Bags of 100 rings can be purchased for $10.00 to $20.00 or 10¢ to 20¢ a ring. A lot of people have been removing the cheap flicker pieces and replacing it with an original Vari-Vue flicker piece. They do look nice but they are not the original configuration and are less collectible. Some dealers claim they are original Vari-Vue chrome rings but they are not. Furthermore, as with the blue ring bases, the flicker pieces are most likely from warehouse finds and were never circulated. So, even though the modern ring may look good, it is actually the least desirable because only the flicker half of your ring is authentic.

In my opinion, the flicker piece should be 75% of the ring value. In other words, a flicker with the "V" ring from China is priced 25% less than a flicker on its original issue silver or gold base. The blue rings should be approximately 10% less. Of course, ring scarcity would be the exception, i.e., a set of Superman or Universal Monsters would be desirable on any setting.

FIVE GREAT FLICKERS

Some of the nicest looking flicker rings include:

1. The Batman - set of 12

2. The Tarzan - set of 6

3. The Looney Tunes - set of 16

4. Apollo 11 & 12 - set of 12

5. Outerspace set (?)

Apollo   **Apollo**   **Batman**

Looney Tunes   **Tarzan**

THE TOUGH ONES

Besides the six or so earliest individual rings, some of the toughest rings to find and hardest sets to complete are:

1. Superman set (?)
2. Universal Monsters - set of 6
3. The Monkees - set of 12
4. Dr. Doolittle set (?)
5. Apollo 11 & 12 - set of 12
6. Marvel Superheros - set of 12

Dr. Doolittle   **Monkees**

Monkees   **Superman**   **Universal**

TOP FLICKER ACTION

(Some of the best flicker action is found on:)

1. Felix the Cat - set of 3
2. McDonald's - set of 4
3. Tarzan - set of 6
4. Looney Tunes - set of 16
5. Frankenberry and Count Chocula rings
6. Arby's Looney Tunes set of 10

Arby's

Arby's

Count Chocula

Frankenberry

Looney Tunes

McDonalds

McDonald's

Tarzan

KING

Of The
COMIC BOOK
PREMIUMS!

In the Summer of 1994, the very rare Supermen Of America prize ring ("Superman prize ring" in collector's short hand) sold for $22,500 in good (GD) condition. This is a new record for a ring in that grade.

But even more significant is the fact that this is the **HIGHEST PRICE EVER PAID** for any comic memorabilia in good (GD) condition. No comic book, premium, toy, or original art has sold for $22,500 in good (GD) condition.

With only ten discovered specimens, the Superman prize ring is on the way to achieving the status of legendary....

Many people ask about the origin and rarity of the prize ring. The following is a detailed explanation of the story behind what many feel is the King of the Comic Book Premiums: the 1940 Superman Prize Ring!

Origin Of The Ring

The Supermen of America club was originally announced in the first issue of *Superman* during the summer of 1939.

To clearly see the relationship of this ring to comic book history, note that just six months before the end of this contest, *Superman* #1 was sent out to eagerly-waiting comic book readers.

Then, as a follow-up to promoting club membership, a contest was held with over 2,000 "dandy free prizes" to be awarded to the winners. The contest consisted of asking Superman Club members to write (in 100 words or less), "What I would do if I had the powers of Superman." On January 28, 1940, this first major superhero-related contest ended.

One of the major prizes was a rather striking silver-finished, gold-topped ring with red accent paint carefully applied around the letter circle on top. The promoters of the contest claimed they would award 1,600 of the rings to the authors of the best 1,600 letters. No one really knows if 1,600 rings were actually given away.

Some historians have questioned this number, speculating that the contest coordinators didn't really have that many rings to give away at all. As was often the case during the '30s and '40s, many comic book related contests exaggerated the number of possible winners. Although this approach used dubious ethics, it is possible that the larger number of prizes offered increased the "size" of the contest and the "hope" of those entering.

The 1940 Supermen Of America membership ring...

the "KING" of the comic book premiums!

Whatever the truth to this unanswered question of collectibles history, the reality is that few specimens survive today!

How Rare Is The Ring?

In 1992, some 50-plus years later, a high grade example of the famous ring sold for an astounding $125,000. The record prices paid for this ring each time one comes up for sale had prompted many collectors to ask, "How rare is the ring?"

Today, only 10 specimens of the ring have surfaced and all of them are presently in the hands of collectors. Seven of the rings grade good (GD) to fine (FN), while the remaining three are very fine (VF) or better.

To add to the issue of scarcity, from 1974 until 1992 there has never been a single one of these rings available. Then in 1992, as the price began to escalate, five rings sold in rapid succession, with each sale establishing a new price record.

Discovery Of Ring #10

Diamond President and CEO Steve Geppi had been running ads offering to buy the ring more than three years. In 1992, Steve received a call from a retired elderly lady… regrettably on the verge of losing her home because of overdue bills.

She told Steve she was sure she had the ring he was looking for… and that it was one of her most treasured possessions. It seems her father had won the ring in the contest way back in 1940 and then gave it to her as a gift.

She wore the ring around her neck for two years after it was given to her, but she decided to put it away for safe keeping when she noticed it had started to show wear. She kept the ring in her jewelry box for more than 50 years! The ring is in average condition.

Thinking the ring might be worth only a few thousand dollars at most, she was pleasantly surprised when Steve offered her $40,000 for it. When Steve made the offer, she happily accepted and promptly paid off her mortgage with money to spare.

More Rings In The Future?

It's likely, as collectors continue to search junk shops, flea markets, and antique shows across the country, a few more examples of the rarity might surface. And with more opportunities for documented sales, only the Shadow knows what higher prices lurk in this ring's future.

But even if the number of rings in the market double, the Superman prize ring will continue to be one of the most historically significant and highly sought-after items in the world of collectibles.

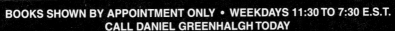

HAKE'S AMERICANA & COLLECTIBLES

AMERICA'S FOREMOST MAIL & PHONE BID AUCTION HOUSE DEVOTED TO NOSTALGIA & POPULAR CULTURE COLLECTIBLES

RINGS & OTHER PREMIUMS OUR SPECIALTY
BUYING & SELLING SINCE 1967

EACH CATALOGUE INCLUDES:
DISNEYANA • COMIC CHARACTER ITEMS • TOYS • RADIO PREMIUMS
WESTERN & SPACE HERO ITEMS • EARLY RADIO & TV ITEMS
ADVERTISING COLLECTIBLES • PRESIDENTIAL CAMPAIGN ITEMS • PINBACK
BUTTONS OF ALL TYPES • SPORTS • MOVIE ITEMS • AVIATION • BICYCLES
AUTOMOTIVE • WORLD WAR I & II PATRIOTIC ITEMS • WORLD'S FAIRS
EPHEMERA • SHIRLEY TEMPLE & RELATED DOLL ITEMS • GUM CARDS

Our bi-monthly catalogues offer a fascinating array of original collectibles. Each "Mail & Phone Bid Auction" catalogue pictures, describes, and gives an estimated value for some 3000 items in the above categories. Bidders participate by sending in a bid sheet and on the closing day of the auction, the status of bids may be checked by phone. We would like to show you what is available—

$7.50 Sample Copy—1 Catalogue
$20.00 Subscription—3 Catalogues
(Overseas: $30.00—3 Catalogues)

P.O. BOX 1444RB
YORK, PA 17405
(717) 848-1333

ILLUSTRATION BY BILL NELSON

PRICES LISTED REPRESENT GOOD AND NEAR MINT CONDITION
(unless otherwise noted)(Rings are arranged and viewed vertically. Arrow pointing down
means follow as links in a set. Arrow pointing up links price to set above)

Addams Family ring set on card, 1964, T.V. (plastic), set of 4 on card (rings & bases produced in different colors) (red, blue, brown, black, amber known)
$150 with card)
Individual rings $3-$6 ea. for amber color
(other colors will bring 50% more)

| Uncle Fester | Gomez | Lurch | Morticia |

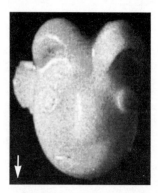

Nigeria

Agent 007
paper, 1960s (black/green)
$8-$20

Congo

West Africa

 African Tribal
1961, (plastic)(set of 6)
(Nabisco Wheat or Rice Honeys)
(called Savage Tribal on cereal box)
$15-$30 each

Agent 007 (1)

French West Africa

Agent 007 (2)

Agent 007 (3)

Congo

Agent 007 Face (paper),
1960s
$8-$20

Agent 007 (4)

↑ **Agent 007 (5)**
paper insert (set of 5)
(blue, green & red bases)
$8-$20 each

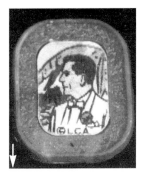

Agent 007 Flicker (1)
Cartooon James Bond in white
sport jacket to a diver underwater in
yellow bathing suit behind a shark

Agent 007 Flicker (1)
ames Bond" to picture of Sean
Connery face.

Agent 007 Flicker(4)
007 gun to picture of Sean Connery
face

Agent 007 Flicker (2)
"007" to picture of Sean Connery
face.

Agent 007 Flicker (5)
"O.S.S." to picture of Sean connery
face.

Agent 007 Flicker (2)
A missile standing on launch pad
inside of a valcano to missile taking off out of valcano opening

Agent 007 Flicker (6)
"633" to picture of agent

↑ **Agent 007 Flicker**
(small round)(6 diff.)
1960s
$8-$20 ea.

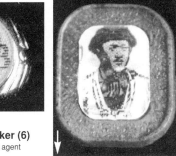

Agent 007 Flicker (3)
"117" to picture of gun.

Agent 007 Flicker (3)
Dark skinned guy with blue hat
strapped onto head to same guy
with veil over face holding a
weapon.

Agent 007 Flicker (4)
Picture of two helicopters (1 yellow, 1 white) to close-up of yellow copter.

Agent 007 Flicker (7)
Face (half white, half flesh with a scar) to same guy being punched "POW".

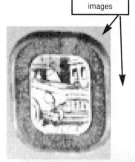

Shows both images

Agent 007 Flicker (5)
"007" gun picture to close-up of James Bond holding his gun.

Agent 007 Flicker (8)
Figure in karate outfit with hands together to same guy defending himself against a kid.

Agent 007 Flicker (10)
Yellow astin martin (sports car) ejector seat with figure shooting of sunroof.

Agent 007 Flicker (6)
Man in white suit with arms behind his back to same man armed with a sword.

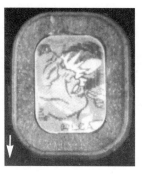

Agent 007 Flicker (9)
Odd-job face to his hat hitting a guy in the head.

Agent 007 Flicker (11)
White yacht cruising to same yacht moved futher along.

Agent 007 Flicker (12)
spaceship in space with cone opening and figure coming out to close-up of figure walking in space.

Agent 007 Flicker
1960s (12 diff., blue base)
$8-20 ea.

Agent 009 Identi-Kit
1960s (card set with 007 ring)
$30-$50 complete

Agent 007 Gun,
1960s
$8-$20

Agent 007 seal
1960s (metal, heavy)
$25-$50

Air Force (plasic)
1950s
$5-$10

Alexander
(see Post tin)

Alice in Wonderl;and
1940s (metal)
$75-$150

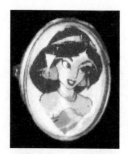

Aladdin - Jasmine
1990s
$5-$10

Aladdin's Lamp
(casino giveaway?)(plastic)
(red/black)
$15-$30

Aladdin's Lamp
(plastic, 1993)
(gumball, yellow base)
$20-$40

Aladdin's Lamp
(plastic, gumball)
$5-$10

Allyson, June
(see Movie Star photo)

Alvin
1960s (plastic)
$25-$50

**Andy Pafco Scorekeeper
Baseball Ring**
1949-Muffets $100-$200

American Airlines
(see Junior Stewardess)

Andy Gibb
(see Movie Star photo)

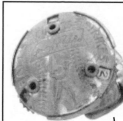

HERE'S YOUR NEW
Andy Pafko
**SCOREKEEPER
BASEBALL RING**

IT RECORDS:
★ OUTS
★ STRIKES
★ BALLS

Personally Autographed by
ANDY PAFKO
Hitting and Fielding Star of the Chicago Cubs

NOW—you can keep an accurate check on every pitch and every play in the ball game—whether you're playing yourself or watching it out at the park or on television.

Just think, your new Andy Pafko Scorekeeper Baseball Ring will never let you get caught napping. If you're an infielder you'll know for sure when to start that double-play and when to play the batter. As an outfielder, you'll always be sure to peg to the right base. Correct, split-second

thinking like that will win many a ball game for you.

You'll want your whole team to have those wonderful, useful new Rings as part of their regular equipment. The attached order blank makes it easy. First, round up the gang! Show them your ring. Then for each additional Andy Pafko Scorekeeper Baseball Ring you want, send just 15c in coin and 1 Muffets box top to: MUFFETS Baseball Ring, Dept. 4, Chicago 77, Illinois.
M-5-49

ORDER BLANK

Muffets Baseball Ring, Dept. 4, Chicago 77, Illinois

Please send me _____ Andy Pafko Scorekeeper Baseball Ring(s). For each Ring I enclose 15c (in coin) and the blue box top from a package of Muffets.

Name _____

Street or R.F.D. _____

City _____ Zone _____ State _____

Supply Limited! Offer Closes September 15, 1949
Offer Good Only in the United States

Andy Pafco paper
(scarce)
$75-100

Andy Panda (plastic)
1990s .50¢-$1

Apollo Flicker (3)

Apollo Flicker (7)

Apollo Flicker (4)

Apollo Flicker (8)

Apollo Flicker (11)
(shows both images)

Apollo Flicker (5)

Apollo Flicker (9)

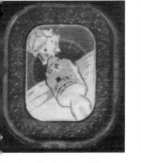

Apollo Flicker (12)

Apollo Flicker (12 diff.)
1960s, Blue base,(scarce set)
$10-$24 ea.

Apollo Flicker (6)

Apollo Flicker (10)

Apollo Flicker (1)
Apollo II logo to "Apollo 11" cartoon figure of all three figures together.

Apollo Flicker (4)
"Edwin E. Aldrin Jr." to face with space suit on (no helmet).

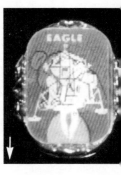

Apollo Flicker (7)
"Columbia" picture to "Eagle" pict

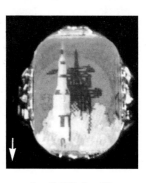

Apollo Flicker (2)
"First Man on the Moon" July 20, 1969 to picture of rocket launching from earth.

Apollo Flicker (5)
"Michael Collins" to face with space suit on (no helmet)

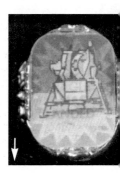

Apollo Flicker (8)
"The Eagle has landed" to pictur Eagle landed.

Apollo Flicker (3)
"Neil A. Armstrong" to face with space suit on (no helmet)

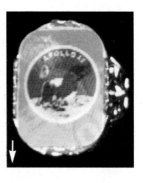

Apollo Flicker (6)
Apollo II logo to picture of Eagle and Columbia docking.

Apollo Flicker (9)
"That's one small step for man, giant leap for mankind" to Armstrong stepping off ladde

Apollo Flicker

Armstrong, Aldrin & Collins photograph faces to picture of Eagle sitting on moon with earth in background
$15-$30

Apollo Flicker (10)
"We came in peace for all mankind" to Armstrong on moon in suit standing by flag.

Arby's Bugs Bunny Flicker

Apollo Flicker (11)
"Apollo 12" angled picture of rocket with moon in background to astronaut stepping on the moon.

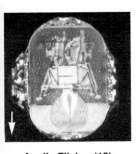

Apollo Flicker (12)
"Apollo 12" picture of ship on moon to ship taking off of the moon.

Apollo Flicker
1960s, (12 diff.)(silver base) (scarce set), $15-$30 ea.

Arby's Daffy Duck Flicker

Arby's Porky Pig Flicker

Archie
1993, Staber
Silver (50 made) - $150
Gold (5 made) - $750

Army (plastic)
1950s, $10-$24

Arthur Godfrey Photo
(See Real Photos)

Arthur Murray Spinner
1976 (Murray Go Round) (Also see
Tom Mix Spinner)
$100-$200

Arby's Yosemite Sam Flicker

 Arby's Flickers
1987 (set of 4)
$20-$40 ea.

Atlanta Crackers
1954 (baseball)
$25-$50

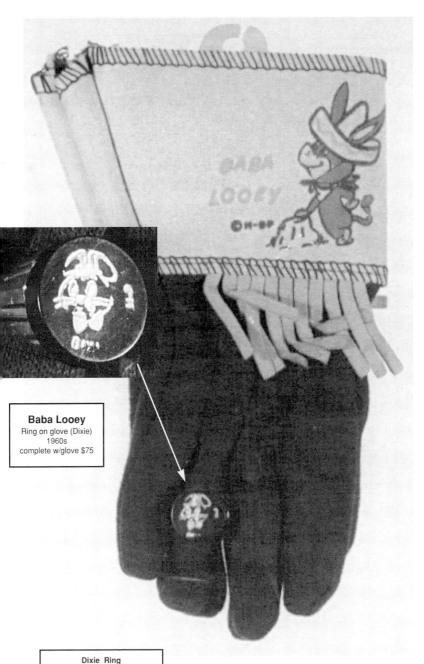

Baba Looey
Ring on glove (Dixie)
1960s
complete w/glove $75

Dixie Ring
(came on Baba Looey
gloves, 1960s
ring only $20-$40

Baba Looey (see Quick Draw McGraw)

Baltimore Orioles World Series
1983, $40-$75

Babe Ruth Club
1934 (gold, metal, Muffets)
$150-$300

Babe Ruth (plastic)
Kellogg's, 1949
$25-$50

Bam!
(paper over plastic) 1976 (DC)
$15-$30

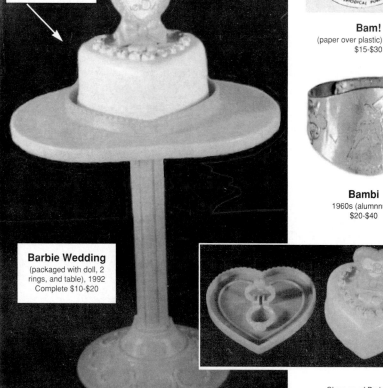

Barbie ring case on ring stand

Barbie Wedding
(packaged with doll, 2 rings, and table), 1992
Complete $10-$20

Close up of Barbie rings (plastic) in case

Bambi
1960s (alumnnum)
$20-$40

Barnabas Collins
(Dark Shadows, T.V.),
Gum, 1969 (2 versions)
$500-$1000

Barney
1993, cloisonne
$3-$6

BARNABAS [OFFICIAL] **RING** FITS ANY SIZE FINGER!

ONLY **50¢** WITH 5 BARNABAS Bubble Gum Wrappers

Send your name, address and Zip Code, with
50 cents and 5 wrappers
TO: BARNABAS Dept. D
P.O. BOX 801, HAVERTOWN, PA. 19083
Offer good only where legal in Continental
U.S.A. Subject to change without notice.

Barnabas Collins (Dark Shadows) gum wrapper paper
(needed to order ring)(in color)(scarce) $75-$100

Barney
1990s, plastic/paper
$0.50-$1.00

Barry Goldwater Flicker
1970s, plastic, blue base
Barry to "I'm for Barry"
$5-$10

Baseball(see Baltimore Orioles, Bowman Gum, Brooklyn Dodgers, Cincinatti Reds, Dodgers, New York Yankees)

Nationals

Red Sox

Baseball
1960s (aluminum)(10 in set)
$10-$20 ea.

Chicago White Sox
(two views shown)

New York Yankees

Baseball
1960 (red, white, blue plastic)(baseb
set of 16)(Kellogg's Shredded Whe
cereal box premium)
$25-$40 ea.
in package - $50

Baseball Centennial
(See Jack Armstrong)

Baseball, Cincinatti Red
1970s, $10-$20

Cleveland Indians

Oakland A's

Detroit Tigers

Orioles

Baseball, New York Me
(metal), 1970s
$20-$40

Baseball Flicker
1960s (modern base)
$2-$5

Cubs Flicker

Red Sox Flicker

Baseball Flicker
1960s (orange base) Cartoon
baseball player swinging a bat
with tree in background.
$2-$5 ea.

Dodgers Flicker

Reds Flicker

Braves Flicker

Orioles Flicker

Senators Flicker

Yankees Flicker

Cardinals Flicker

Pirates Flicker

 Baseball flicker
1960s (set of 10)
(candy premium)(gold base)
$15-$30 each

FUN TO PLAY–GET STARTED!

Here's how: Choose up sides—even number of players on each team. Lead-off batter puts on ring, keeping the "diamond" level. Pull back "bat" spring and . . . SNAP! You hit a "homer," a "single"—or maybe an "out"!

Be sure "bat" is back. (Caution: Pull back only slightly. No pressure required.) and ball is centered at home plate before swinging.

If ball lands in hole marked 0, batter is out.
If ball lands in hole marked 1, it is a single.
Double is made by hitting ball into hole 2.
Triple by hitting ball into hole marked 3.

A "homer" is scored by hitting the ball straight up the middle into farthest hole marked HR.

If ball does not land in any hole, it counts as 1 strike against batter. If ball rolls back to home plate a foul (strike) is counted. 3 strikes and batter is out.

Each team gets three outs. Regulation game, nine innings. Use handy score card to keep record. For extra fun, give each team a name such as Yankees or Cubs. Form a regular league and play "double headers" and night games.

SCORE CARD NAME	1	2	3	4	5	6	7	8	9	R	H

GET EXTRA RINGS! ORDER FOR YOUR FRIENDS.
MAIL COUPONS ON BACK!

IT'S FUN TO EAT A "BIG LEAGUE" BREAKFAST WITH

Oh boy, crispy flakes of the best-tasting cereal of *all*—real Kellogg's Corn Flakes! Fresh, sweet and crunchy in a bowl of cool milk with sugar and fruit on top. . . . spoon in *deep!* Every . . . as supply food-energy . . . Eat Kellogg's Corn . . . you'll be glad you did.

Kellogg's CORN FLAKES

Baseball Game paper
page 1 & 2 (scarce)- Both pages
$80-$100

BLANK

. . . .
. . . . . York 46, N. Y.

. . . . Play BASEBALL GAME
. . . . nclose one Kellogg's Corn
. . . . age) and 25 cents in coin.
(No stamps, please.)

MY NAME (please print)_____

MY ADDRESS_____

CITY_____ZONE____STATE____

GIVE THIS TO A PAL
(As a Kellogg friend you may invite a chum to share this special premium offer.)

. . . .

"KELLOGG'S INVITATION CLUB"

KELLOGG'S, Box 291, New York 46, N. Y.

Yes, I'd like to join the fun, too. Please send me (   )
BASEBALL GAME RINGS. For each I enclose one
Kellogg's Corn Flakes box top (any package) and
25 cents in coin. (No stamps, please.)

MY NAME (please print)_____

MY ADDRESS_____

CITY_____ZONE____STATE____

In Canada send 25¢ in coin and 1 Kellogg's Corn Flakes
box top to: Kellogg's, Dept. S-BL, London, Ontario

BATTER UP!

HERE'S YOUR NEW
PLAY BASEBALL
GAME RING

DIRECTIONS AND SCORE CARD INSIDE!

Basketball
(metal base)
1960s, $50-$100

Bat
1960s, metal
$20-$40

Bat
(plastic) in package
1960s (glows in dark)
(Black & white bat versions)
$20 each in package (sealed)
$10 ring only

Bat
1960s (plastic)(vending machine)
without package $5-$10

Batman Bat Signal
1990s (c.1964) (metal, w/sparkl
(Rosecraft on card)(DC)
$10-$20

Batman Bat Signal
(Party)(plastic), 1982(DC)
$1

Bat & Fink Ring Paper
1960s (vending machine paper)(in color)
$15-$25

Batman Bat Signal
(Diamond Comics Distr.),
14k gold w/diamond chips
(25 made), 1992(DC)
$2000

Batman
1966 (green rubber) (DC) $2-$4

Batman Bat Signal
(metal), 1990 (DC)
$10-$20

Batman Bat Signal
(plastic), 1990s, (c.1964)
(Rosecraft on card)(DC)
$25-$50

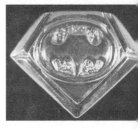

Batman Bat Signal
(Diamond Comics Distr.),
silver (550 made) 1992(DC)
$250

Batman Flicker (1)
"Member Batman Ring Club" to full
figure "Batman/Robin" side by side.

Batman Game
1960s (plastic w/dome)
$15-$30

Batman Disc
(paper on plastic), 1960s
$12-$25

Batman Figure
(metal)(color, painted)
1990s, $5-$15

Batman Flicker (2)
"Batman" face to "Robin" face

Batman Clock Flicker
1960s (silver base)
$25-$50

Batman Flicker
Batman photgraph face (Adam
West) to Robin photograph face
(Burt Ward), 1960s
$25-$50

Batman Flicker (3)
"Batman" chest view up to "Bruce
Wayne" chest view up.

BATMAN
Flicker Pictures

6 Different
Pictures of
Batman and
and Robin
in this
Machine.
Collect
them all!

Batman Flicker Ring Paper
1966 (vending machine paper)(rare)(in color)
$20-$35

Batman Flicker (4)
"Robin" chest view up to "Dick
Grayson" chest view up

Batman Flicker (5)
"Batman" face to full figure swinging
on rope.

Batman Flicker (6)
"Robin" face to full figure swinging
on rope

Batman Flicker (7)
"Batmobile" to Batman & Robin swinging on ropes dropping into the Batmobile

Batman Flicker (10)
"Joker" face to "POW" fist punching jokers face.

Batman Flicker (1)

Batman Flicker (8)
"Batcopter" to close up of Batman & Robin in Batcopter

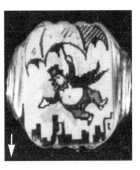

Batman Flicker (11)
"Penguin" full figure holding umbrella to full figure floating down with open umbrella

Batman Flicker (2)

Batman Flicker (3)

Batman Flicker (9)
"Riddler" face to "BAM" Batman & Riddler fighting

Batman Flicker (12)
"Batman" face to Batwoman

↑ **Batman Flicker**
(Original silver base)
(set of 12), 1966
$10-$25 ea.

Batman Flicker (4)

Batman Flicker (5)

Batman Flicker (9)

Batman Gold
(14K gold)(DC)
1990s, $30-$60

Batman Flicker (6)

Batman Flicker (10)

Batman Gold Face
(3D, metal)(DC)
$25-$50

Batman Flicker (7)

Batman Flicker (11)

Batman Logo
1990s, (metal, blue/gold))(DC)
$5-$10

Batman Flicker (12)

↑ **Batman Flicker**
(blue base)(DC)
((set of 12), 1966
$10-$20 each

Batman Flicker (8)

Batman Logo
(Nestle's), 1980s (red)(DC)
(round)(see Robin), $25-$50

Batman Logo
(round) (blue)Nestle's
1980s(DC)
$25-$50

Batman (plastic bat), 1970s
$10-$20

Batman
1970s
(plastic)(black/yellow)
$10-$20

Batman Prototype
1993, (metal)
$600

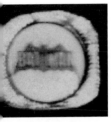

Batman Logo
(square)(D C)
Nestle's (1980s)
$25-$50

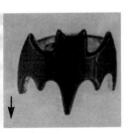

Batman (metal)

Batman
(metal) (3 diff.), 1966 (on card)
Complete on card (DC)
on card $60-$125 ea.
Ring only $15-$30

Batman Collapsible (rubber bat),
glows-in-dark)(blue, red & black versions)
1970s
$25-$50 each

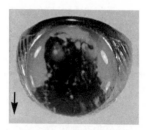

**Battlestar Galactica
(Alien)**

**Battlestar Galactica
(Commander Adama)**

**Battlestar Galactica
(Daggitt)**

**Battlestar Galactica
(Silon)**

↑ **Battlestar Galactica**
1978 (universal Studios)
(metal)(photo) (4 in set)
$20-$40 each

Bazzooka Joe Baseball
1950s (metal), $30-$60

Bazooka Joe Initial
1940s (gold color, black top)(scarce)
(also used as popsicle premium)
$200-$400

Bazooka Joe Printing Stamp
1940s, $60-$120

Beany
1960s (propeller top/
compass base (plastic)
complete $150-$300

Beatles
1960s (Metal)
$5-$10

**Beatles
(George)**

**Beatles
(John)**

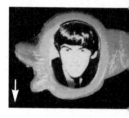

**Beatles
(Paul)**

**Beatles
Ringo**

↑ **Beatles** (plastic)
(photo)(set of 4)
1964 (red, blue, yellow,
green colors known)
$8-$15 each

**Beatles Flicker
Ringo**

↑ **Beatles Flicker**
1960s (set of 4)(gold metal
base)(purple, green, red
& black flicker versions)
$20-$30 each

Beatles Flicker (Paul)
Paul to "I'm Paul" - "Beatles"

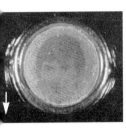

**Beatles Flicker
George**

**Beatles Flicker
(George)**
George to "I'm George" - "Beatles"

**Beatles Flicker
(Ringo)**
Ringo to "I'm Ringo" - "Beatles"

↑ **Beatles Flicker**
(Silver base) (set of 4)
$8-$15 each

**Beatles Flicker
John**

**Beatles Flicker
(John)**
John to "I'm John" - "Beatles"

**Beatles Flicker
(George)**

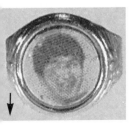

**Beatles Flicker
Paul**

Beatles Flicker (Paul)

Beatles Flicker (Ringo)

Beatles Flicker (John)

Beatles Flicker
(Blue base) (set of 4), 1966
$5-$10 each

Beetle Bailey
1993 (silver) Staber
(20 made) - $200

Belt Buckle
(western)
1950s (metal, silver)
$30-$60

Belt Buckle
(western)
1950s (metal, gold color)
$30-$60

Betty Boop
1990s (metal cloisonne)
$20-$40

Betty Boop
(12 on card,
generic)
1990s,
$20 (set)

Betty Grable Photo
(See Real Photos)

Billy The Kid Saddle
(see Saddle...)

Billy West Club
1940 (see Tom Mix Circus &
Cowboy Riding Horse)
$50-$150

Bing Crosby Photo
(See Real Photos)

Black Flame
(Hi Speed Gas), 1930s (metal)
$125-$250

Bob Hope Photo
(See Real Photos)

Boo Berry
(see Frankenberry & Count
Chocula), 1980s (cereal)
$75-$150

Boot (see cowboy boot)

Bowman Gum
(Pirates; one for each
baseball team) 1949(also see
Football, Bowman)
$100-$200

Boxing Flicker
1960s. Two full figure box-
ers in the ring punching
each other.
$5-$10

Boy Pitching Tent Flicker
1960s (plastic)
$5-$10

Boy Scout
(silver)(metal)
1940s, $25-$50

Bozo (See Clown)

Bozo's Circus
1960s, $50-$100

Bozo Figure
1980s, $10-$20

Brer Fox Club
1938 (metal)(rare)
$75-$200

Broncho Rider Flicker
1950s (thick top lens)
$30-$50

Brooklyn Dodgers
(see Dodgers)(scarce), 1940s,
$100-$250

SPINNER

1. Cut all parts from frame.
2. Put small part in clamp on ring.
3. Snap two halves of disk together, secret compartment or whistle.
4. Insert large pin all the way, into both holes in disk.
5. Grasp small pin between finger and thumb and spin.
6. To wear as ring, push spinner into hole on ring.

SPINNER

1. Cut all parts from frame.
2. Put small part in clamp on ring.
3. Snap two halves of disk together, secret compartment or whistle.
4. Insert large pin all the way the other two both holes in disk.
5. Grasp small pin between finger and thumb and spin.
6. To wear as ring, push spinner into hole on ring.

Broom Hilda Spinner
(on tree, in package), 1970s
$60
Ring put together: $30-$50

IMPORTANT: Read these instructions before ordering prizes!

Send only red tops from 7-oz. red and-white Grape-Nuts Flakes packages. We cannot accept tops from 1-oz. Grape-Nuts Flakes or any size Grape-Nuts packages. Send orders to Buck Jones, c/o Grape-Nuts Flakes, Battle Creek, Mich. Print name and address plainly. Order prizes by name and number. Make sure you send correct number of box-tops for each prize. If prize comes in choice of colors or sizes, state color or size wanted. Be sure to put on correct postage. When sending 5 or more tops, put them in separate package and have it weighed at post office for correct postage. Do not include any writing in package. Just print plainly your name and address on outside of package. Then send order for premiums in a separate letter, and print plainly your name and address on the envelope. When sending a large number of box-tops you can save postage by mailing them third class mail (in unsealed package). All prizes can be obtained with Grape-Nuts Flakes box-tops without sending money. WE PREFER THAT YOU SECURE YOUR PRIZES IN THIS WAY If you do not want to wait to get all box-tops needed, send in number of tops and amount of money indicated. This offer expires Dec. 31, 1937. Good only in U. S. A.

A TIP FROM BUCK

"WHEN it comes to grub for breakfast, there's nothing hits the spot with me like a heapin' bowlful of Grape-Nuts Flakes. They're the crispest, crunchiest, eatenest flakes I know. A real he-man treat! And they're mighty good for you, too. Served with good rich milk or cream and fruit, Grape-Nuts Flakes pack more varied nourishment than many a hearty meal. Ask your mother to get some right away."

A Post Cereal made by General Foods

Buck Jones Club paper
(scarce) $50-$75

Brownies
(Several different stores)
1930s (metal)
$100-$250

No. 402. Membership Ring. A beauty! 24-carat gold finish. Good-luck horse-shoe design. Adjusts to fit any finger. Free for 3 Grape-Nuts Flakes box-tops.

"WHOOP-EE-EE!"

says
BUCK JONES

FREE PRIZES
for every boy and girl
who joins my club!

Buck Jones Club Ring
(Grape Nuts), 1937
$75-$150

uck Rogers Birthstone
(Cocomalt), 1934
$200-$400

Buck Rogers Photo
1940s, $150-$300

Buck Rogers Repeller Ray
1930s (Cream of Wheat), (green stone)
Good - $750
Fine - $1500
Near Mint - $3000

ou remove the source of energy (by king the ring away from the light), hat happens? The electrons slip back to their old places again. And when ey do, energy is created that turns into isible light! When the ring gives off this ght, it glows in the dark.

he light is a "cold" light, however. It oesn't send its rays any distance. This eans that it can be seen only at close ange. It's invisible to people standing nly a couple of dozen feet away.

hat's about enough of this technical alk, don't you think? But we did want to ive you a short explanation of why the uck Rogers Ring of Saturn has these mazing qualities.

HOW YOU CAN HAVE FUN WITH YOUR RING

Now what you want to know is "how can I have fun with my Buck Rogers ring?" Well, there are plenty of ways.

First of all, you can use it as a secret signal to flash on your pals. You and other Buck Rogers fans can recognize each other *in the dark* with your magic-glow rings. (Just the way Buck used it to tell his friends from the Neptunians.) Even on a pitch-black night, your Buck Rogers ring will glow so you and your pals can recognize each other instantly as members of the gang. And remember

—you have to be up close to see the light from the ring. So while you're showing your ring to a friend near you, people 25 feet away won't see a thing. Pretty neat, isn't it?

Here's another way you'll find your magic ring mighty handy. You can use it to "talk" to your friends in the dark *without making a sound*. Just work out a set of signals—a secret code like the ones used in various lodges, fraternities, and underground societies. Then by passing your hand over the ring, so as to cover up its glow and then let it "flash," you can pass on information to a friend looking on without saying a word to him.

For instance, two "flashes" might mean "Danger—let's get out of here." Three flashes could mean, "Go back and round up more of the gang—we need help." It's easy to work out a code in advance to cover whatever emergencies you think you and your pals might run into.

Incidentally, if some one of your friends hasn't gotten his Buck Rogers ring, better suggest to him that he send for it right away so he can be in on the fun, too. (Just tell him to send a dime and a Post's Corn Toasties boxtop to Buck Rogers, Battle Creek, Michigan.)

You'll think of lots of other ways in which this amazing ring really will be valuable. So now go ahead and have fun with your Buck Rogers Ring of Saturn!

6382 Printed in U.S.A.

the MAGIC POWER OF THE RING OF SATURN is yours!

Buck Rogers Ring Of Saturn Paper
(see next page)

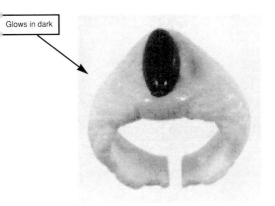

Glows in dark

Buck Rogers Ring of Saturn
(red stone)(Post)
1940s, $325-$850

Also see Jack Armstrong
Dragon's Eye, Shadow Carey Salt
and Shadow Blue Coal

THE BUCK ROGERS RING OF SATURN

Ever see anything like the Buck Rogers ring before? Bet you haven't. It's really a wonder ring. It has magic qualities that make it glow in the dark with mysterious blue light. You'll have plenty of fun with it!

You heard on the radio how the Ring of Saturn helped Buck Rogers save Dr. Huer from the people on Neptune. That's how valuable it can be! You, too, will find plenty of ways where the ring will be mighty handy. We'll talk about some of them a little later on.

In the meantime, we want to let you in on the secrets of this miraculous Ring of Saturn—tell you what's behind its mysterious properties.

WHY DOES IT GLOW?

You already know how to make it glow. Just wear it awhile in the light. It can be sunlight or light from an electric lamp—it doesn't matter. Then take the magic ring into a dark room, and PRESTO! It glows.

Now *why* does it glow? It hasn't any batteries or wires. The fact is, it doesn't depend on electricity for its light. The light it sheds is really a kind of energy, though, just as electricity is a kind of energy.

Here's what happens. When you let the sun shine on this ring awhile, or let it stand under an electric light, the ring absorbs light energy—it's called *radiant* energy.

ATOMIC SECRETS

Energy takes many forms. You've rea about atomic bombs. What gives the their terrific explosive power? It's cause by a sudden release of energy—energ that rushes out when the tiny particle which make up uranium atoms a, pushed out of place. These tiny atom particles are called electrons, proton and neutrons. When you study chemi try, you'll find that everything in th world is composed of atoms—billion and billions of them.

Now to get back to your Buck Roger ring—it's made up of atoms, too. Rad ant energy (light energy) is powerf enough, in its own way, to push electror out of their normal positions in th atoms of the ring material. Then whe

Buck Rogers Sylvania Bulb
(glows-in-dark) (Sylvania)
1953 - (rare)
Good- $750
Fine - $1500
Near Mint- $3000

Buffalo Bill Jr
1950
$30-$60

Buck Rogers Ring Of Saturn Paper
(scarce), 1940s
$50-$100

Bugs Bunny Dome
1980s (small)(metal)
$10-$20

Buffalo Bill
(plastic),
1950s $15-$30

Bugs Bunny Bullseye
1990 (paper disc)
$8-$15

Bugs Bunny Face
1980s (metal), $5-$10

Bugs Bunny Face
1992 (metal)
$10-$20

Bugs Bunny Face
1980 (metal cloissine)
$10-$20

Bugs Bunny Face
1970s (plastic)(blue over white)
$15-#30

Bugs Bunny Figure
1980 (metal cloissine)
$12-$25

Bullet Pen
(metal, generic), 1940s (very rare)
(Robbins archives)
$300-$600

**Bugs Bunny
Indian Headress**
1993 (Warner, metal)
$30-$60

Bullwinkle
1969 (Jay Ward display
(in color) $35-$70

Bugs Bunny Ski
1980 (metal cloisonne)
$10-$20

Burt Lancaster picture
1950s (Kelloggs)
$10-$20

**Buster Brown
Big Foot Whistle**
1950s (plastic), $20-$40

Buster Flicker, side 1

Tige Flicker, side 2
**Buster Brown Club
Flicker**
(Buster to Tige), 1950s
$30-$60

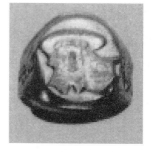

Buster Brown Club
1940s (metal)
$30-$60

Buzz Corey Space Patrol
(plastic) 1950s (photo)(rare)
$125-$250

Buster Brown
1920s (metal, scarce)
$150-$300

Buzz Corey (Carol)
sidekick (photo),1950s
$125-$250

Calgon Soap
1950s (metal)(bathtub)
$75-$150

Canada Dry
(Smilin Jack)(plastic)
$50-$100

Cap Gun Ring
(See RinGun)

Captain
(see Post Tin)

Captain Action Flicker (
Full figure Capt. Action to full
figure CA logo
$20-$30

ptain Action Flicker (2)
l figure Capt. Action to full figure
Aquaman
$20-$30

Captain Action Flicker (5)
Full figure Capt. Action to full figure
Capt. America
$20-$40

Captain Action Flicker (8)
Full figure Capt. Action to full figure
Lone Ranger
$20-$40

aptain Action Flicker (3)
ll figure Capt. Action to full figure
Batman
$20-$40

Captain Action Flicker (6)
Full figure Capt. Action to full figure
Flash Gordon
$20-$40

Captain Action Flicker (9)
Full figure Capt. Action to full figure
Phantom
$20-$30

aptain ActionFlicker (4)
ll figure Capt. Action to full figure
Buck Rogers
$20-$40

Captain Action Flicker (7)
Full figure Capt. Action to full figure
Green Hornet
$30-$60

Captain Action Flicker (10)
Full Figure Capt Action to full figure
Spiderman
$30-$60

Captain Action Flicker (11)
Full figure Capt. Action to full figure
Steve Canyon
$15-$30

Captain Action Flicker (2)

Captain America
(metal), 1980s (in color)
$50-$100

Captain Action Flicker (12)
Full figure Capt. Action to full figure
Superman
$20-$40

Captain ActionFlicker (11)

Captain America Moo
1977 (metal)
$100-$250

Captain Action Flicker (13)
Full figure Capt. Action to full figure
Tonto
$20-$40

Captain Action Flicker (12)

Captain Bill
1940s (Hills Brothers)(scarce)
$75-$150

↑ **Captain Action Flicker**
(silver base)(13 in set), 1960s
priced individually

↑ **Captain Action Flicker**
1960s (blue base)(13 in set)
$10-$25 ea.

Captain Caveman
1980s (metal cloissone)
$10-$20

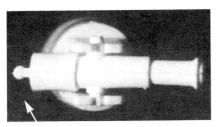

Captain Crunch
1970s (similar to Crazy ring)
(no indentation on side of base)
$40-$80

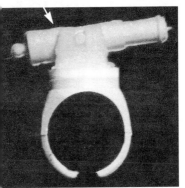

Captain Crunch Cannon
(cereal), 1970s (plastic)
$40-$80

Captain Crunch Whistle
(cereal), 1970s (2 views)
$30-$60

**Captain Crunch
Compass**
(cereal) 1970s
$50-$100

Captain Crunch Figural
(cereal), 1970s (plastic)
$150-$300

Cap'n Frosty Flicker
1960s "Cap'n Frosty" to "Dairy Clipper"
$10-$20

Captain Hawks Air Hawks
1930s (metal)
$75-$150

**Captain Hawks
Sky Patrol**
1930s (metal)(rare in NM)
$75-$200

Example in
good condition

Compass

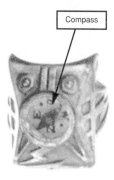

Captain Marvel
1940s (rare)(metal)
Good - $625
Fine - $1250
Near Mint - $2500

**Captain Midnight Flight
Commander paper**
(see next page for price)

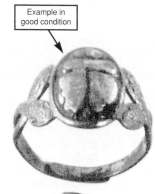

Green top | Example in
near mint condition

Officer's Emblem Ring

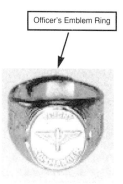

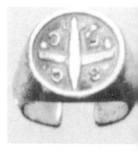

Captain Hawks Secret Scarab
1937 (rare)(rare in NM)
(Post Bran Flakes)(Same as
Melvin Purvis SecretSarab)
(green top)
Good - $375
Fine - $750
Near Mint - $1500

**Captain Midnight
Flight Commander**
1941 (Ovaltine)(metal)
$200-$450

**Captain Midnight
Flight Commander
Signet** (Ovaltine)
1957 (plastic)(rare in VF-NM)
$400-$1000

BE A SECRET SQUADRON FLIGHT COMMANDER!
USE THIS CARD TO SEND FOR YOUR OFFICER'S EMBLEM RING!

DEAR CAPTAIN MIDNIGHT:

I want to become a Flight Commander and wear an Officer's Emblem Ring! To qualify, I have lined up three new members for the Secret Squadron. I have printed their names and addresses on the back of this card. Please send them each their Secret Squadron Membership Code-O-Graph Badges and Secret Code Books. I am enclosing the three Ovaltine seals my three friends gave me, and also 10c in coin to help cover the cost of handling and mailing my officer's Emblem Ring and Flight Commander Booklet. Please send my Ring and Booklet as soon as you can.

MY OWN NAME AND ADDRESS:

NAME...

ADDRESS..

TOWN...STATE.................

MAIL TO: Captain Midnight's Secret Squadron, 360 North Michigan Avenue, Chicago, Ill.

INSERT DIME HERE

Remember Also to Enclose Three Ovaltine Seals!

YOU GET THIS BEAUTIFUL *Officer's Emblem Ring*

When You Become a Secret Squadron Flight Commander!

Captain Midnight Flight Commander
paper, 1941
complete $50-$75

Top contains a mirror placed diagonally enabling viewer to see at 90 degrees.

Top removes to reveal stamp pad for printing

Captain Midnight Look Around (Ovaltine), 1942
(Same As Lone Ranger & ROA Mystic Eye)
$50-$175

Captain Midnight Initial Printing (Ovaltine), 1948 (metal)
$150-$500

Captain Midnight Marine Corps Paper
(see next page)

YOUR OFFICIAL MARINE CORPS EMBLEM RING
and the Famous Fighting Service You Honor by Wearing it!

★ ★ ★ ★ ★

HERE is your own personal Marine Corps ring. It bears the official insignia of the United States Marines, the oldest and proudest and "fightingest" military service in America. I want you to wear this ring always. It is the Secret Squadron's way of honoring the Marine Corps, and showing those brave Soldiers of the Air, Land and Sea that we admire everything they stand for.

What the Marine Emblem Means

The raised design on the face of your ring is the official emblem of the U. S. Marine Corps. The *globe* means that the Marines are always ready to go into place in the world where duty calls them. The *anchor* means they are "Soldiers of the Sea," working closely with the U. S. Navy. The *eagle* means they are "Soldiers of the Air" as well. The Marines have their own flying units, operating with each of the two Fleet Marine Forces, in the Atlantic and in the Pacific.

The Marine Motto and Colors

The motto of the Marines is "Semper Fidelis," two Latin words which mean "Always Faithful." The Marine Corps has proved true to this motto throughout its history. The official colors of the Corps are Scarlet and Gold.

The Marine Hymn

From the Halls of Montezuma,
To the Shores of Tripoli;
We Fight Our Country's Battles
On the Land as on the Sea
First to Fight for Right and Freedom
And to Keep our Honor Clean.
We are Proud to Claim the Title of
United States Marine

Our Flag's Unfurled to Every Breeze
From Dawn to Setting Sun
We Have Fought in Every Clime and Place
Where we could take a Gun.
In the Snow of Far Off Northern Lands
And in Sunny Tropic Scenes,
You will find us always on the Job —
The United States Marines.

Here's Health to You and to our Corps
Which we are Proud to serve.
In Many a Strife we've Fought for Life
And Never Lost our Nerve.
If the Army and the Navy
Ever Look on Heaven's Scenes,
They will find the Streets are Guarded by
United States Marines.

The Story of the Hymn

This song of the "Soldiers of the Sea" is believed to have been written in 1847, during the Mexican War. An unknown poet of the Marines set his words to a tune from an old French opera, and this immortal fighting song was born. Many changes have been made in the words during the past century, but there has been no change in the dauntless spirit of the men who sing them. They are still "proud to claim the title of United States Marines."

FAMOUS SAYINGS
of the U. S. MARINES

* * *

The French were retreating at Chateau Thierry, and a French officer asked if the Americans were not going to follow "Retreat?" said a captain of the Marines "We just got here!" The Marines stayed

*

At Belleau Wood a famous slogan was born when Sergeant of Marines Dan Daly, a hero of many battles, shouted to his men, "Come on—do you want to live forever?"

*

Richard Harding Davis, famed war correspondent, is credited with coining the apt expression, "The Marines have landed, and the situation is well in hand."

*

A detachment of Marines under Major James P. Devereux fought in the heroic defense of Wake Island. When contacted by radio and asked what they wanted most urgently, they replied with the

---

THE MARINES
* IN THE AIR *

The Marine Corps has distinguished itself on land, at sea, and in the air. The aviation units which are a part of each Fleet Marine Force have served with telling effect over both oceans. Marine fliers are trained by the Navy

Marine airmen are among the world's "toughest" and most capable fighters. They are trained to operate from ground bases in regular land warfare, from aircraft carriers at sea, and to support landing parties on hostile shores. The Marine Corps also has barrage balloon units to protect vital properties. Other units are trained as parachute troops, and others to make landings either on land or water in new-type amphibian gliders.

Every day we hear of new exploits of the United States Marines. We are proud to honor them by wearing the ring which bears their official emblem!

Capt. Midnight
"SS-1"

Published at
SECRET SQUADRON HEADQUARTERS
360 N. Michigan Ave.
Chicago, Ill.

THE STORY OF
THE
UNITED STATES
MARINES

> SEMPER FIDELIS

By
CAPTAIN MIDNIGHT

Captain Midnight Marine Corps paper
1942 (scarce), $100-$125

Captain Midnight Marine Corps (Ovaltine), 1942 (metal)
$150-$450

Captain Midnight Mystic Sun-God Paper
1940s, $75-$100

YOUR NEW OFFICIAL S.S. RING
Celebrating our Secret Squadron Adventures
in Mexico, Ancient Home of the Aztecs

Every organization has an official ring for its members, bearing insignia derived from campaigns or exploits in which the organization has performed outstanding service. Here is your very own official Secret Squadron ring. I hope you will wear it always as a mark of your membership in the Secret Squadron, and as a reminder of our Secret Squadron adventures in the land of the Aztecs, of which this ring is a symbol.

The Aztecs, as you may know, lived and reigned long ago in the country we now know as Mexico. Like most ancient people they worshipped many gods. Their best-known god called TONATIUH, the Sun God is shown as the Aztecs pictured him on the side of your ring. Montezuma and other famous kings of the Aztecs worshipped this Sun God as the giver of all power and made human sacrifices to him on the high altar of the Sun God's temple.

The red plastic stone in your ring symbolizes the altar of the Sun God's temple. Its rich, brilliant color simulates the deep red glow of a genuine ruby.

Although the Aztecs were masters of such sciences as astronomy and mathematics they

believed in many superstitions who savage or childish today. One of t stitious signs, the sign for "good lu was believed to safeguard the weare below the picture of the Sun God on of your ring.

But your new official Secret Squad far more than simply a handsome rin teresting Aztec designs. It contains a special feature you will find of great i in Secret Squadron activities an secret compartment carefully concea "outsiders" cannot possibly discover

This secret compartment, cleverly neath the stone in your ring, can be to you in carrying secret information a it along to friends who will seem to o merely examining your ring. Directions for opening this secret compartment are given on the next page. I know you will guard this secret by showing the hidden compartment only to loyal friends of the Secret Squadron.

Capt. Midnight
"SS-I"

The Story of Your
SECRET SQUADRON

MYSTIC

SUN-GOD RING

by
CAPTAIN MIDNIGHT

HOW TO USE THE
▓ECRET COMPARTMENT

RING
CLOSED

RING
OPEN

▓ace your thumb against the side of the stone
▓ectly above the shaft of your ring. Press
▓ntly   and watch the stone slide out, revealing
▓ hidden compartment underneath. Note how
▓u can hide a short note written on thin paper
▓ pass along to a friend who knows the secret
▓ the hidden compartment and how to open it.
To close your ring, simply press the stone
▓ck in place. Be sure the edges of the stone
▓ in the metal grooves at the sides.

Published by

▓CRET SQUADRON HEADQUARTERS
360 N. MICHIGAN AVENUE
CHICAGO, ILLINOIS

Captain Midnight paper
1947
$100-$150 (complete)

Red plastic stone symbolizes the alter of the sun god's temple

**Captain Midnight
Mystic Sun-God
Ring** (Ovaltine),
1947 (metal/plastic)
Good $525
Fine $1050
Near Mint $2100

Mailing package for Mystic Sun-god ring

SECRET SIGNALS

To Be Used Only By Owners of Captain
Midnight's "Whirlwind" Whistling Ring

("Whit" means a short blast. "Wheee", a long one.)

"Whit, Whit, Whit, Wheee"..The "V" signal,
for victory.
Means "Every-
thing is Okay.
Our Side's Win-
ning!"

"Wheee, Whit, Whit!".....Danger! Watch
Out! Enemy pres-
ent!

"Wheee, Whit, Wheee, Whit!"..Come here! I
need help!

"Whit, Whit, Whit, Whit!".. Hurry! Hurry!
Hurry!

"Whit, Wheee, Whit, Whit!"..Lie low! Keep out
of sight!

"Wheee, Wheee, Wheee!"....O. K.! Come out
of hiding!

"Whit, Whit, Wheee, Whit!"..Fun! Come on out
and play!

Now remember to keep the above signals absolutely
secret! Learn them perfectly so you can use them at
any time, in any place!

Here is

YOUR OWN NEW

"Whirlwind"
Whistling Ring

from

CAPTAIN
MIDNIGHT!

**Captain Midnight Whirlwind
Whistling Ring paper**
1940, $60-$80

The Story Behind Your "WHIRLWIND" Whistling Ring

> 5-blade propeller-type air-turbine that whirls inside when you blow thru the holes in the top

THIS amazing new whistling ring is a vast improvement over any so-called whistling ring you've ever seen.

Here's how it is better. First, it is beautifully designed so that you can be proud to wear it all the time, to amaze your friends and to have always at hand when you want to give important signals. The design on the face of the ring represents a radial-type air-cooled airplane engine, and the wings on the side stand for the Spirit of Aviation.

The second advantage is the new 5-blade propeller-type "air-turbine" that whirls inside the ring when you blow into the holes in the top. This turbine is specially balanced so that it produces the same musical tone as all other rings sent out by Captain Midnight, so his friends can always recognize each other by the sound of

their whistling rings. Also, this balanced air-turbine will keep whirling freely a long time after you have stopped blowing, "whirring" like a regular air raid siren!

The third special feature of this ring is that you don't have to take it off your finger to blow it! You just press against the inside edge of the ring with the tip of your thumb, so the whistling part is raised slightly from your finger, and then blow for all you're worth! For best results, be sure your lips don't close over the side vents.

So that's the story of your "Whirlwind" Whistling Ring. Now turn to the back of this folder and read about the secret signals to use in sending important messages to other friends of Captain Midnight! Learn all the signals by heart!

Captain Midnight
Whirlwind Whistling
(Ovaltine), 1941 (metal)
$150-$525

Captain Midnight Whirlwind Whistling Paper
1941, $60-$80 (complete)

Captain Midnight
Skelly Oil (red V)(metal)
1940s., $75-$200

Captain Planet Ring
1990s (on card)
on card - $10
ring only - $3-$6

Captain Planet Sound Ring
(on card), 1991 (gold & silver versions)
Complete - $40
Ring only - $7-$25

Captain Planet
(on card) (all rings are plastic with diff. designs)
(1990s) - $10 ea., ring only $3-$6

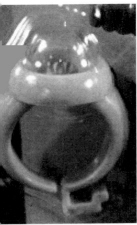

Captain Planet
(6 diff.) 1990s
$3-$6 ea.
(not on card)

Both saucers are identical except one has florescent paint on underside. Aluminum metal

Complete ring has string wrapped around top. Pulling string releases saucer to flight

Captain Video Flying Saucer
(base only), 1951
$50-$200

Captain Video Flying Saucer
(gold, aluminum & nickel base versions, 2 saucers) (one glows in dark)(two diff. saucer sets exist w/plastic glow-in-dark & metal glow-in-dark versions), Post Toasties and Powerhouse candy premium 1951(rare with saucers & pull string)
$750-$1200 complete

Captain Video Flying Saucer
Day saucer only $300-$400
Night saucer only $400-$600

ALL THE FLYING SAUCER RINGS YOU WANT!
ONLY 20c plus two POWER HOUSE wrappers for each set
• 1 ring   • 1 night saucer   • 1 day saucer

ALL THE EXTRA FLYING SAUCERS YOU WANT!
ONLY 10c plus two POWER HOUSE wrappers for each set of three
• 1 night saucer   • 2 day saucers
Mail To: POWER HOUSE, P.O. Box 31, New York 13, N.Y.

POWER HOUSE, P.O. BOX 31, NEW YORK 13, N.Y.

For ordering rings:
Please send me postage-paid, _____ Flying Saucer Rings. For each ring I enclose twenty cents (20c) in coin plus two POWER HOUSE CANDY BAR wrappers.

For ordering extra flying saucers:
Please send me postage-paid, _____ sets of extra Flying Saucers. For each set I enclose ten cents (10c) in coin plus two POWER HOUSE CANDY BAR wrappers.

PRINT NAME AND ADDRESS:

Captain Video Flying Saucer ring paper (scarce)
1951, $100-$120

NAME_____
STREET_____
CITY_____
ZONE_____STATE_____
Offer good only in U.S. and may be withdrawn at any time. Offer void

CAPTAIN VIDEO
COMES THE
FLYING SAUCER RING
FOR NIGHT AND DAY FLIGHTS
IT'S A MYSTERIOUS RING!
A GAME OF SKILL!

Look Rangers HERE'S HOW

TO MAKE YOUR
Flying Saucer Ring Perform Best

Step A Push end of power cord through hole in power shaft. When end shows through, wind in the direction of arrow on top of red launching spinner. Wind tight.

Step C Keep fist clenched, g string *strong, steady* pul don't jerk. The harder pull, the higher it goes! luminous saucer at nigh plain saucer, daytime.

Step B Place flying saucer over the top of the power shaft. Be sure that the side of saucer marked "Flying Saucer" is *UP*. You are now all set for launching.

Super Charge Super-charge your nig flying saucer by holdin under electric light or ye flashlight a minute or t before launching. Makes glow brighter in the da

TRY THESE FOR EXTRA FUN!

- When you play rescue and adventure games, launch flying saucers as signals to your ga
- Have regular contests to see whose flying saucer goes highest—farthest—stays up lon
- Use glow-in-the-dark saucer as a squadron night signal sender and secret identifier.
- Learn to spot-land your saucer—work out landing competitions with other teams.
- See below how you can get extra kits or saucers to build-up a regular squadron.

IMPORTANT: Mark your name or secret sign on all your saucers for identificatio

DID YOU KNOW—that Post Toasties is Captain Video's favorite corn flakes? That's right! So Captain Video is glad to cooperate with Post Toasties in making these genuine Flying Saucer Rings available to you and your friends.

Better take a tip from the Captain—and always ask Mom for Post Toasties, the Heap Good Corn Flakes!

☞ SPECIAL OFFERS! ☜

1. EXTRA COMPLETE KITS for yourself and for your friends so you can form a flying saucer squadron and have more fun! Only 20¢ and one Post Toasties boxtop for a complete Flying Saucer Ring kit: including ring, power cord, and 2 saucers—1 for daytime, 1 that glows in the dark.

2. NOW! 4 FLYING SAUCERS ONLY 10¢. Only 10¢ and one Post Toasties boxtop for 4 saucers—2 for daytime, 2 that glow in the dark for night flying.

"Flying Saucer" name permitted by Zenith Corporation, Clinton, Missouri

Use this handy Order Blan

CAPTAIN VIDEO, BOX 0, ST. PAUL, MINN.

For ordering complete kits:

Please send me postage-paid ____ Complete Flying Saucer Ring ki each kit I enclose twenty cents (20¢) in coin plus one POST TOAS boxtop.

For ordering extra Flying Saucers:

Please send me post-paid ____ sets of 4 extra Flying Saucers (2 time, 2 nighttime). For each set I enclose ten cents (10¢) in coin an POST TOASTIES boxtop.

PRINT NAME AND ADDRESS:

NAME_____

STREET_____

CITY_____

ZONE_____STATE_____

Offer expires March 31, 1952. Offer good only in U. S. A. This offer ve any state, territory or municipality where prohibited, taxed or othe restricted.

**Captain Video Flying
Saucer Ring paper**
1951, $100-$120

Captain Video Pendant
1950s (rare)

complete w/film
Good - $500
Fine - $800
Near Mint - $1000

Subtract $75-$100 if ring base is missing. If picture is missing, reduce price by 80%

(also see Major Mars Rocket)

Captain Video Pendant Paper
1950s
$150-$200

WEAR IT AS A RING . . . OR CARRY IT IN YOUR POCKET

Press the square plug on top of the ring shank into the cut-out square under the Rocket, and wear your Rocket as a ring. Or use the chain to attach the Rocket to your belt loop, or to carry keys.

ATTACH HERE

GLOW-IN-DARK IDENTIFICATION

Captain Video's own picture in the top compartment of the Rocket glows in the dark. It proves, day or night, that you are a secret Video Ranger.

SECRET ALARM AND SIGNAL WHISTLE

Your Rocket is a secret whistle. Blow into the mouthpiece, being sure not to cover the hole near the mouthpiece. You can make up your own secret danger signals and secret code messages of long and short blasts.

DO NOT COVER THIS HOLE

SECRET MAGNIFYING GLASS

LIFT OUT

Only Video Rangers know that the little window in the Rocket Compartment is really a strong magnifying glass. Every Guardian of Law and Order carries a magnifying glass to check fingerprints and clues that can't be seen with the naked eye.

Captain Video Photo
1951
$100-$350

Captain Video Paper
(see next page)

ALWAYS GET POWERHOUSE . . . THE MOST DELICIOUS CANDY BAR WITH THE MOST VALUABLE WRAPPERS.

HERE'S YOUR POSITIVE IDENTIFICATION

YOUR IDENTIFYING NUMERALS

Your identifying numerals are stamped inside your SECRET SEAL RING. Remember, no other Ranger has the same number as you!

CAPTAIN VIDEO'S OWN SEAL

Notice the circle in the center of the ring. It's stamped with Captain Video's own seal. Whenever you write a secret message, use this seal. All you do is slip a corner of the paper under the loose circle. Then, press down hard on the circle with your thumb. The imprint of the seal will be proof that your message is from a Video Ranger.

Get everyone in your gang to register under the heroic banner of Captain Video. Remember, the SECRET SEAL Ring not only gives foolproof identification, it adds more fun to adventure games. So don't let the coupon on the next page go to waste —pass it on to a friend!

TO GET THE SECRET SEAL RING

MAIL ONLY 15c

plus either — two 5c POWER HOUSE WRAPPERS

or — one 10c POWER HOUSE WRAPPER

Mail to POWER HOUSE, P.O. Box 135, NEW YORK 46, NEW YORK

POWER HOUSE, P.O. BOX 135, NEW YORK 46, NEW YORK

Please send me, postage-paid, _____ SECRET SEAL RINGS. For each ring, I enclose fifteen cents (15c) in coin, plus either two wrappers from 5c size POWER HOUSE CANDY BAR—or one wrapper from the 10c size.

PRINT NAME AND ADDRESS

NAME_____

ADDRESS_____

CITY_____

ZONE_____ STATE_____

Offer good only in U.S. and may be withdrawn at any time. Offer void in States and Localities which prohibit or restrict such transactions.

FROM CAPTAIN VIDEO TO HIS AGENTS

THE

SECRET SEAL RING

FOR FOOLPROOF IDENTIFICATION

----- CUT ON DOTTED LINE -----

IDENTIFICATION CARD

This card certifies that the bearer, answering to the earth name of:

PASTE YOUR PICTURE HERE

(sign your name here)

(your address)

is entitled to wear the Secret Seal Ring

showing identifying numerals_____
(fill in your ring number)

CAUTION: carry this card with you wherever you go. Show it only to other Video Rangers or to Police officers if you need assistance.

Captain Video Secret Seal Paper
1951, (scarce) $250-$500

Captain Video Secret Seal
1951, (copper top)(gold base), (metal)
$200-$600

Captain Video Secret Seal
(gold), 1951 (metal)
$150-$500

Care Bears
1983 (plastic/paper)(yellow base)
$2-$4

Carrot Ring
1960s (3 diff.)
$5-$10 ea.

Casper Figure
(plastic) 1950s (cereal)
$15-$30

Casper The Friendly Ghost Flicker
1960s, Casper walking to Casper flying (original silver base)
$10-$40

Casper The Friendly Ghost
(see Universal Monster Flicker Set)(the 2 Casper flickers may have been part of this set)

Casper Face
1991 (plastic)(black over white)
$5-$10

Casper The Friendly Ghost Flicker
(2 diff.), 1960s (blue base)
$10-$20 ea.

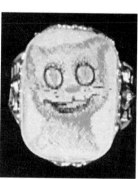

Cat Flicker
1960s
$2-$4

Casper Figure
1990s (plastic)(black over white)
$30-$60

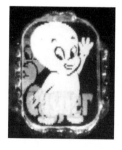

Casper The Friendly Ghost Flicker
1960s Casper waving to Casper peeking from the corner (original silver base)
$10-$40

Casper Figure
1970s (metal)
$50-$100

Cat Flicker
1960s (round)
$2-$4

Cat Woman
1991 (metal cloisonne)
Rosecraft
$20-$40

Charlie Chaplin
1940s (rare)
$100-$250

Charlie McCarthy
1940s (metal)
$200-$425

Charlie McCarthy Photo
(see Real Photos)

Chilly Willy
1980s (metal (in color)
$5-$10

Chandu The Magician
1940s (metal)
$75-$150

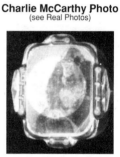

Chee-Chee Flicker
"Chee-Chee" to gorilla sitting
on a log(original base)
$10-$30

Chicago White Sox
(see Baseball)

Chilly Willy Face
1980s (metal)(cloisonne)
$10-$20

Charles Starrett Photo
1950s (square) (cereal)
$20-$40

Charles Starrett Photo
(see Real Photos)

Chief Wahoo
1941 (Goudy Gum),
(also see Indian)
$75-$200

Chilly Willy Face
1980s (plastic)(blue over white)
$2-$4

China Clipper
1936 (Quaker(gold color metal)
$30-$100

Cincinatti Reds
(baseball), 1970s
$10-$20

Cisco Kid Hat
1950s (rare)
$200-$600

Cisco Kid Saddle
(see saddle)

Cinderella
1960s (aluminum)(Disney)
$30-$60

Circus
(see Lucky Horseshoe)

Chuck & Cheese
1990s
$1-$2

Cisco Kid Secret Compartment
1950s (rare)(metal)
Good - $1875
Very Good - $2810
Fine - $3750
Very Fine - $5625
Near Mint - $7500

Cisco Kid Club
(gold & silver color
versions)(metal)
$100-$300

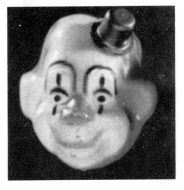

Clarabelle Face/Hat
1950s (rare)
Good - $375
Fine - $750
Near Mint -$1500

Chumley
1960s (plastic)(black
over white)
$100-$200

Clarabelle Horn
1950s, (rare in VF-NM), $125-$450

Clown Face Flicker
Clown face moving happy to sad
$4-$10

Coca Cola
1994 (metal, gold color)
(staber)
$10-$20

Cleveland Indians
1950s, $50-$100

Cling and Clang
(see H.R. Puff 'n' stuff)

Clown Flicker
1960s (gold metal)(Hong Kong)
$4-$10

Coca Cola
1994 (staber, metal)(gold color)
$10-$20

Compass
(see Black Flame,
Captain Crunch, Cocomalt,
Davy Crockett, Nabisco
& Wheaties)

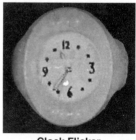

Clock Flicker
1960s (blue & yellow
base versions)
$3-$5 ea.

Clown Flicker
1950s (thick top)
$20-$60

Compass Ring
1950s
$20-$60

Clock Flicker
1960s (green base)
$10-$20

Clyde Beatty Lions Head
(Quaker Crackles)
1930s (rare)(jewel in mouth)
$200-$450

Compass Ring
1950s
$20-$60

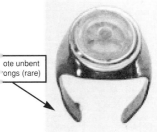

ote unbent
rongs (rare)

Compass, Cocomalt
1936 (metal)(rare example
w/unbent prongs
$50-$100

Cousin Eerie
(Warren) 1960s (metal)
(gold color)(also see
Uncle Creepy)
$30-$100

Cowboy Hat (Goudy)
1940s
$20-$40

Compass, Nabisco
1950s (gold w/ red dial)
$20-$50

Cowboy Flicker
1950s (thick top)
$20-$40

**Cowboy
Riding Horse**
1950s (silver)(gumball)
$5-$20

**Cowboy
Riding Horse**
(see Billy West Club &
Tom Mix Circus)

Compass, Wheaties
1940s
$20-$40

Cowboy Flicker
1950s (metal)(in color)
$20-$60

Cowboy Riding Horse
(gold version)
(gumball), 1950s
$5-$20

Count Chocula Flicker
1980s (dancing)(see Boo
Berry & Frankenberry)
$50-$75

Cowboy Boot
1940s (Goudy Gum)
$20-$60

Cowboy Ridging Horse
(silver version)
(gumball), 1950s
$5-$10

Cowboy shootout flicker
1960s (plastic)
$2-$4

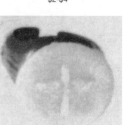

Crackerjacks Airforce
secret compartment
1940s
$10-$30

Crazy Rings
(see Quaker)

Creature (see Universal Monsters)

Cub Scout
1950, $30-$75

Cupid (see Heart-Arrow &
Valentine Flicker)

Daffy Duck (see Arby's...&
Looney Tunes)

Dagwood
1993 (Staber)(Silver(only
18 produced))
$200

Dairy Clipper Flicker
(see Cap'n Frosty)

Dancing Flicker
1970s (metal)(in color)
$4-$8

Dancing Flicker
1960s (plastic)(red, & blue
base versions)
$4-$8 ea.

Dancing Girl flicker
1960s (plastic)(red & blue
base versions)
$4-$8

Dark Shadows
(see Barnabas Collins)

Dancing Male Flicker
1960s (plastic)(red &
blue base versions)
$4-$8

Daniel Boone
(plastic), 1960s (Kelloggs)
$10-$20

Davey Adams
(Lava) (siren), 1940 (metal)
(scarce)
$175-$425

**Davy Crockett
Compass**
(elastic band) 1950s
$150-$375

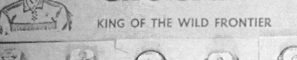

KING OF THE WILD FRONTIER

Davy Crockett
Fess Parker photo
rings on board (24 rings)
$225

Davy Crockett Face
(raised) (platic), (yellow,
red), 1950s
$20-$60

Davy Crockett Face
(raised)
1950s, $20-$60

**Davy Crockett Fess
Parker figure photo**
1960s
$10-$40

Davy Crockett Face
(green enamel), 1950s
$40-$100

Davy Crockett Figure
1960s
$10-$30

Davy Crockett Face
(metal), 1950s
$20-$60

Davy Crockett Face
(raised) (silver)
1960s, $20-$60

Davy Crockett Figure
(silver), 1950s
$20-$60

Davy Crockett Figure
(silver) (oval), 1950s
$20-$60

Davy Crockett Face
(metal), 1950s
$30-$80

**Davy Crockett
Fess Parker head photo**
1960s
$10-$40

Davy Crockett
(blue enamel), 1950s
$50-$100

Davy Crockett Face
(square, brass), 1950s
$20-$60

Davy Crockett Figure
1960s
$10-$30

Davy Crockett Flicker,
T.V. Screen (scarce)
1950s
$300-$600

Davy Crockett Head
(gold) (plastic), 1950s
$20-$60

Dennis O'Keefe Photo
1950s
$10-$20

Dennis The Menace (Joey)
1960s (plastic)(Black over orange)
$20-$40

Davy Crockett Head
(bronze) (plastic)
1950s
$20-$60

Dennis The Menace (Dennis)
1960s (plastic)(silver over blue)
$20-$40

Dennis The Menace (Margaret)
1960s (plastic)(silver over red)
$20-$40

Davy Crockett Head
(silver((plastic)
1950s
$20-$60

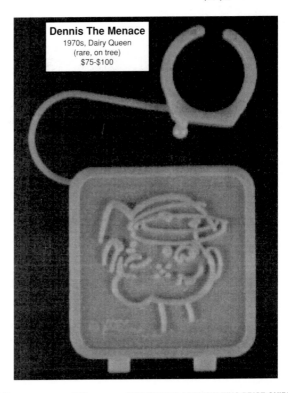

Dennis The Menace
1970s, Dairy Queen
(rare, on tree)
$75-$100

Davy Crockett Rifle
(silver or bronze), 1950s
$20-$60

Dennis The Menace (Ruff)
1960s (plastic)(Black over yellow)
$10-$30

Detroit Tigers
1970s
$10-$20

Devil Dog
(movie) Quaker, 1938
(gold color metal)(rare in NM)
$75-$200

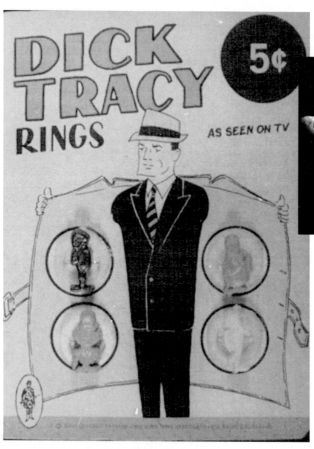

Dick Tracy Card
1966 (plastic)(4 rings)(black, blue, green,
red & yellow ring versions)
complete on card - $150, rings only - $15-$25 ea.

Coggles
(from card)

Dick Tracy
(from card)

Flat Top
(from card)

Prune Face
(from card)

Dick Tracy Characters
1966 (plastic, came on card)
(black, blue, green, red & yellow
ring versions)
$15-$25 ea.

**Dick Tracy
Crimestoppers**
1991
in box game - $50
ring only - $20-$35

**Dick Tracy
Figure**
1970s (plastic)(red
over white)
$10-$25

Hemlock Holmes
(from card)

**Dick Tracy
Movie**
1993 (plastic)(Black
over yellow)
$3-$5

Joe Jitsu
(from card)

Dick Tracy Hat
1930s (var. exists w/enamel hat)
(hat painted green)
$150-$400

Dick Tracy Monogram
1930s (rare)(metal)
Good - $400
Fine - $800
Near Mint - $1600
Note: A proto-type exists from
Robbins warehouse

Dinosaurs (5 diff.),
1970s
$2-$4 ea.

Gold colored
brass

Top of ring
removes to
reveal secret
compartment

**Dick Tracy Secret
Compartment**, 1940s (metal)
$200-$500

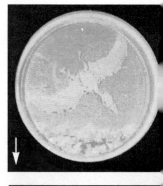

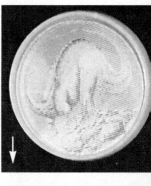

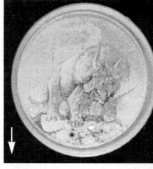

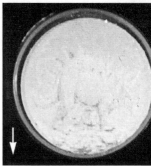

Mickey

Pluto

Minnie

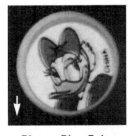

Snow White

↑ **Disney (Sugerjets)**
(9 diff.), 1950s (plastic)
$40-$80 ea.

↑ **Dinosaur Flicker**
1980s (set of 6)(plastic)
$2-$4 ea.

Donald

Peter Pan

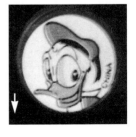

Disney Disc, Daisy

Dumbo

Pinnochio

Disney Disc, Donald

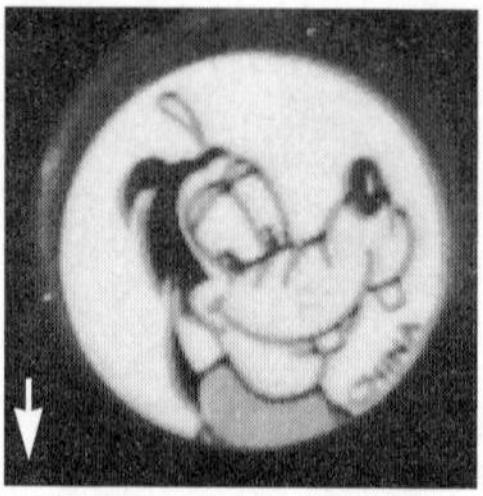

Disney Disc, Goofey

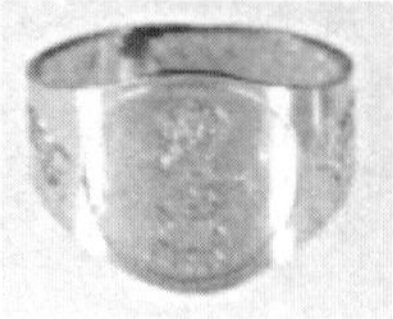

Dixie (Hanna-Barbera)
(aluminum), 1960s
$15-$30

Dixie (see Baba Looey & Huckleberry Hound & Jinx)

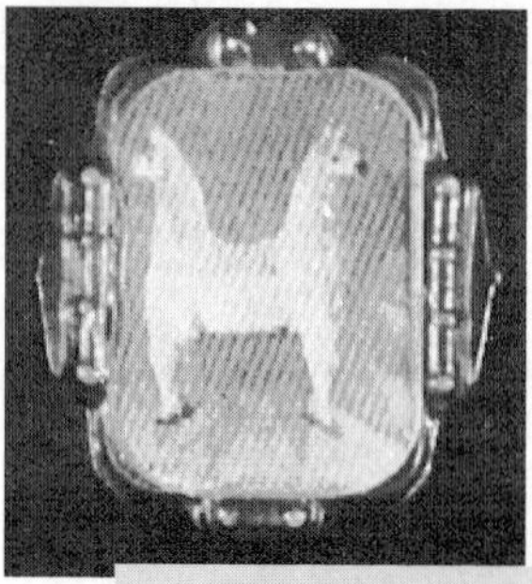

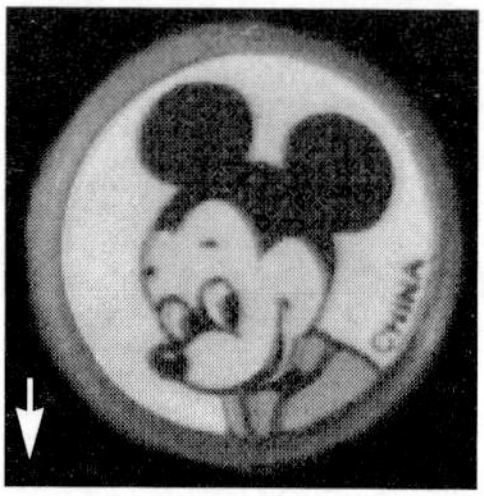

Disney Disc, Mickey

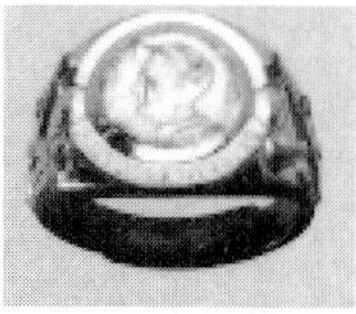

Dizzy Dean
(Win With)(metal)
(Post Grapenuts), 1936
$75-$175

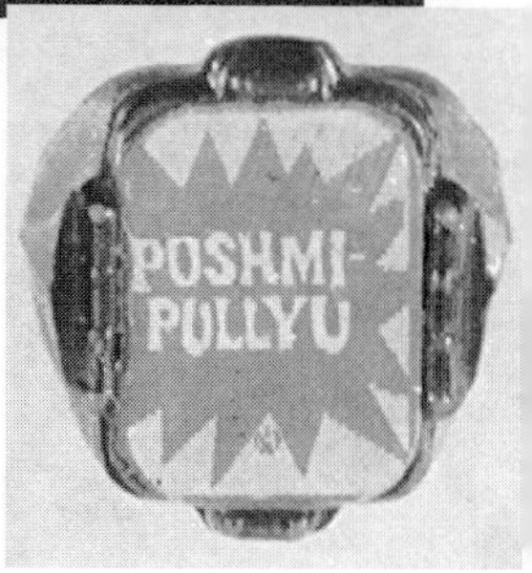

Doctor Doolittle Flicker
Pushmi-pulyu, 1970s (both images shown)
$20-$60

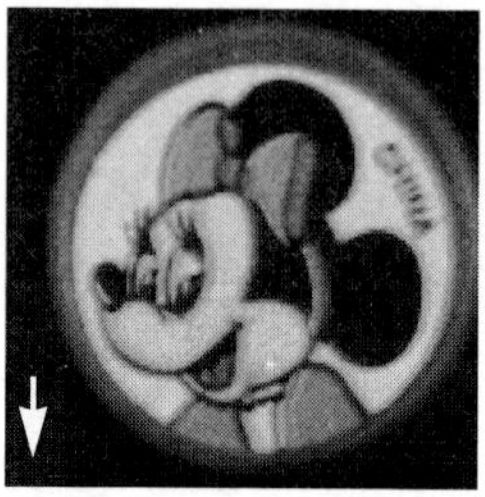

Disney Disc, Minnie

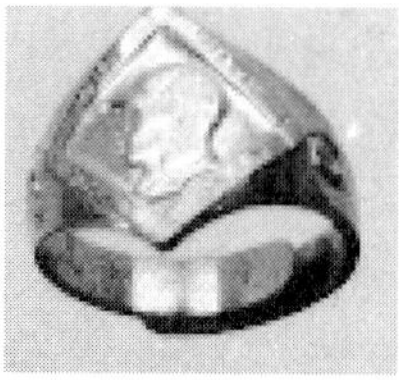

Dizzy Dean Winners
(Post Grapenuts), 1936 (metal)
$75-$175

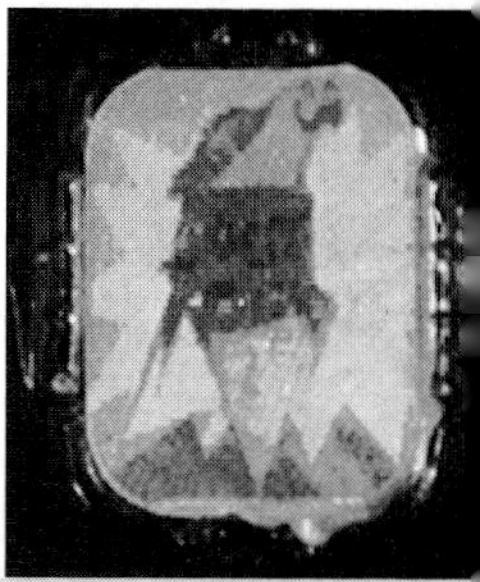

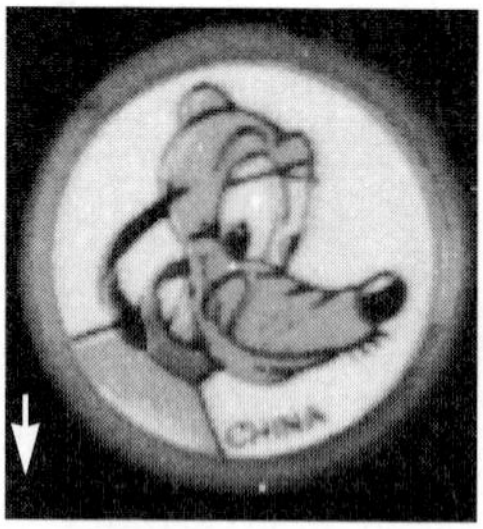

Disney Disc, Pluto

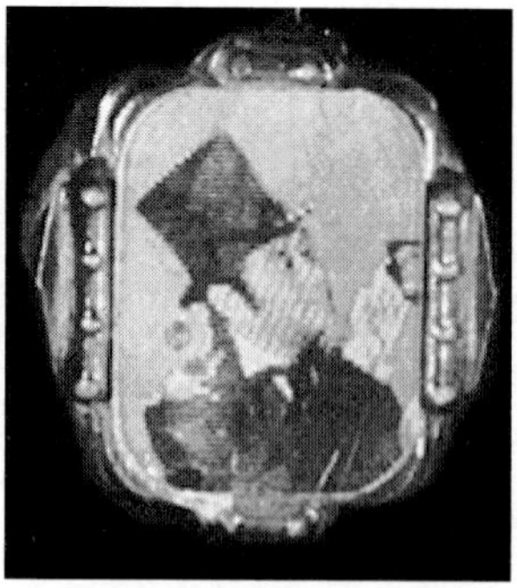

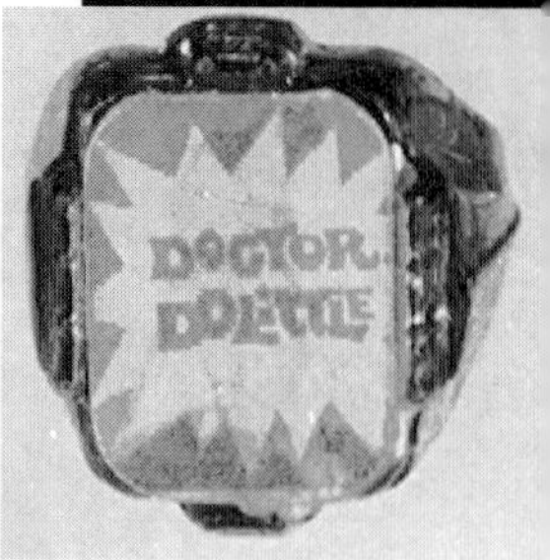

↑ **Disney Disc**
1990s (plastic)(set of 6)
$1-$2 ea.

Doctor Doolittle Flicker
Dr. Doolittle to Horse, 1970s
$20-$60

Doctor Doolittle Flicker
1970s (both images shown)
$20-$60

Doctor Doolittle Flicker
1970s (Dr. Doolittle face to
"Jip" face of dog)
$20-$60

Dodgers (see L.A. Dodgers)

Don Winslow Member
(Kelloggs), 1938 (metal)
(each ring carrys its
own serial number)
Good - $300, Fine - $600, Near Mint -$1200

Donald Duck (See
Disney Disc and Ingersoll)

Baby Donald
1980s, $3-$6

Donald Duck Face
1980s (metal cloisonne)
$15-$25

Donald Duck Big Face
1980s
$1-$2

**Donald Duck Small
Face,** 1990s
$5-$10

**Donald Duck
Small Face**
(2 diff.), 1990s
$5-$10 ea.

Donald Duck Face
1980's
$3-$6

Donald Duck Face
(3d, metal in color)
$40-$100

Donald Duck Face
(red face)(gold & silver face
versions), 1980s
$8-$15

Donald Duck Figure
(metal cloisonne)
$10-$30

Donald Duck Figure
1930s (pewter)(1st Donald ring)
$70-$150

Donald Duck Figure
1980s, (metal, painted)
$15-$30

Donald Duck Figure
1990s
$5-$10

Donald Duck Figure
1930s (metal w/color)
$70-$150

Donald Duck
(glow-in-dark) (Sterling)
color & plain,
round & square top
1950s
$40-$100

Donald Duck Figure
(small, metal cloisonne)
$5-$10

Donald Duck Figure
1970s
$10-$20

Donald Duck
(glow-in-dark)
(square top, color &
plain) 1950s
$40-$100

Donald Duck
Good Luck Portrait
1950s
$50-$100

Donald Duck Living Toy Paper (see next page)

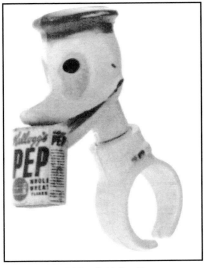

PEP box is a magnet which makes Donald move as if he were alive

Donald Duck Locket
(metal, round)
$10-$40

Donald Duck Locket
(oval, metal)
$10-$40

Donald Duck Living Toy
(with magnetized Pep box)
1949
$250-$400 complete
ring only - $150-$250
Pep box only - $150

YOUR ORDER BLANK

KELLOGG'S, Dept. 424, New York 46, N. Y.

Yes, I want (   ) more DONALD DUCK "LIVING TOY" RINGS. For each one I enclose a Kellogg's PEP box top and 25 cents in coin. (No stamps, please)

MY NAME_____
(Please print)

MY ADDRESS_____

CITY_____ZONE_____STATE_____

GIVE *THIS* TO A PAL — (As a Kellogg friend you may invite a chum to share this special premium offer.)

KELLOGG'S "INVITATION CLUB"

KELLOGG'S, Dept. 487, New York 46, N. Y.

Yes, I'd like to join the fun, too. Please send me (   ) DONALD DUCK "LIVING TOY" RINGS. For each one I enclose a Kellogg's PEP box top and 25 cents in coin. (No stamps, please)

MY NAME_____
(Please print)

MY ADDRESS_____

CITY_____ZONE_____STATE_____

(Offer expires July 31, 1950)

Oh Boy! Oh Boy! Oh Boy!

Here's Your NEW Movable, Mysterious

DONALD DUCK

"Living Toy" Ring

TURN QUICK ➔

Donald Duck Living Toy Paper
1949 (rare) $100-$150

Donald Duck Locket
(heart, metal)
$10-$40

Donald Duck
(sterling, square, no color),
1950s
$40-$100

Door Knocker
(see salesman)

Dorothy Hart
1940s (metal)(rare in NM)
$150-$350

Douglas DC-6
(cereal), 1950s
$30-$60

**Douglas F-3D
Sky Knight**
(cereal), 1950s
$30-$60

Douglas MacArthur
(see Real Photos)

Dracula (see Universal
Monsters)

Dukes of Hazzard
(Hazzard County Police)
(plastic), 1983
$20-$60

Dudley Do-Right
(see Rocky & Bullwinkle)

Dudley Figure
(metal cloissone)
$20-$50

Dudley Figure
(metal, painted)
$40-$80

Dudley on Horse
(metal cloissone)
$20-$50

Dynomutt
(metal, cloissone)
$20-$50

Ed Sullivan
(see Real Photos)

Elizabeth Taylor
(see Movie Star photo)

Elmer Fudd Flicker
(see Looney Tunes)

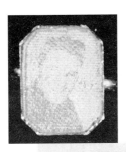

Elsie The Cow
1950s (plastic)
$15-$30

Elvis Flicker
(Elvis to Pricilla Presley)
1960s, (gold base)(Hong Kong Star)
$5-$20

Elvis Flicker
(Elvis Presley to Patsy Kline)
1960s (metal)(Hong Kong Star)
$20-$60

Elsie The Cow
1950s (plastic)(gold on white)
$15-$30

Eric Estrada
1980s, (Chips)(plastic)(yellow)
$2-$4

Elvis Flicker
1960s, $60-$120

Elvis Flicker
(Elvis Presley (blue) to Patsy Kline (red)) 1960s, (blue)(metal)
(Hong Kong Star)
$20-$60

Eisenhower/Johnson Flicker
1960s (black flicker)
(Hohn Kong Star)
$15-$40

E.T. Face
(movie), 1992 (metal)(Universal)
$4-$10

E.T. Heart
1992 (metal)(Universal)
$4-$10

Eye Flicker
1960s (in color)(Hong Kong
Star)(v-base silver)
$4-$10

E.T. Face
(movie, 1982)(Universal)
on card - $150
ring only - $50-$125

E.T. Love
1982 (Universal)
$20-$50

E.T. Logo
1982 (metal cloissone)(Universal)
$20-$50

Explorer's (see Fireball Twigg)

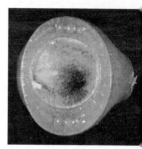

Eye Flicker
1960s (plastic)(red & blue
base versions)(B&W eye)
$3-$8

E.T. Face I Love
1992 (metal cloissone)(Universal)
$5-$10

Eye Flicker
1960s (gold metal base)
(Hong Kong Star)
$5-$10

E.T. Face-Hat
1982 (metal cloissone)
(universal)
$20-$50

Eye Flicker
1960s (in color)(Hong Kong
Star)(Silver base)
$4-$10

Eye Blinking Flicker
1960s, (Picture of an eye to
same eye closed as if blinking)
$5-$10

Fang
1960s (plastic)(silver over blue)
$40-$90

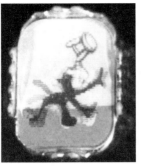

Felix Flicker
Felix swinging a bat
(set of 3.) (silver base)
$15-$40 ea.

Felix Flicker
Felix kicking a football
(set of 3) (silver base)
$15-$40 ea.

DR/George Washington Flicker
1970s (Hong Kong)(metal)
$10-$20

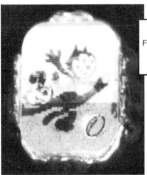

Felix Flicker
Felix balancing a chair on his nose
(3 in set) (silver base)
$15-$40 ea.

Femforce, Ms. Victory
1994 (metal, in color)(1st comic
book premium ring offer in over
4 decades)
$15-$20

Felix Flicker (3 diff.)
1960s (blue base)
$15-$30 ea.

Felix Face
1970s, (in package)
in package - $30, ring only - $10-$20

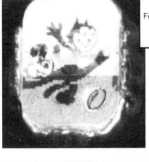

Femforce, Synn
1994 (metal, in color)
$10-$14

WRAP ME AROUND YOUR FINGER

ORDER YOUR
MS. VICTORY RING
TODAY!

THE FIRST <u>TRUE</u> COMIC BOOK
PREMIUM RING IN FIFTY YEARS!
THIS HIGH QUALITY METAL RING
FEATURES FULL COLOR ENAMEL
DETAILING, AND IS <u>ONLY</u> AVAIL-
ABLE THROUGH THIS ONE TIME
SPECIAL OFFER. HURRY! ...WHILE
SUPPLIES LAST!

Femforce Ring
from comic book series
1994

Other rings in series
Nightveil
She-Cat
Stardust
$10-$14 ea.

YES! PLEASE ENTER MY ORDER
FOR AN EXCLUSIVE MS.
VICTORY® RING. I'VE ENCLOSED A CHECK
OR MONEY ORDER (NO CASH) FOR $10.95
PLUS $2.25 S&H AND THIS ORIGINAL
CERTIFICATE (NO COPIES WILL BE
ACCEPTED.) FLORIDA RESIDENTS ADD 7%
SALE TAX.

_____ SIGNATURE _____
PLEASE SEND MY RING TO:

NAME

ADDRESS

CITY/STATE/ZIP

PLEASE ALLOW 6-8 WEEKS FOR DELIVERY. ALL
ORDER SUBJECT TO ACCEPTANCE. OFFER EX-
PIRES AUGUST 31, 1994 OR WHILE THE SUPPLIES
LAST

Rhett '93

MAKE CHECKS PAYABLE TO AND ORDER FROM: THE GREAT AMERICAN RING CLUB, P.O. BOX 300546, FERN PARK, FL., 32730-0546

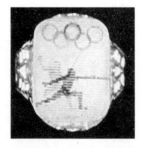

Fencing Flicker
1970s (metal)(Hong Kong)
$4-$10 ea.

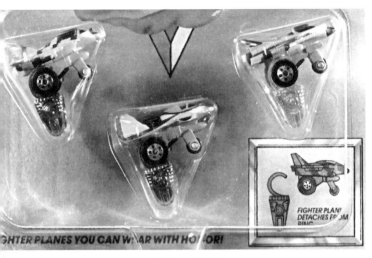

Finger Fighters
(3 diff.) 1989
complete in package - $25, ring only - $3-$6

Side I

Fireball Twigg Paper
1948
$75-$100

Side I

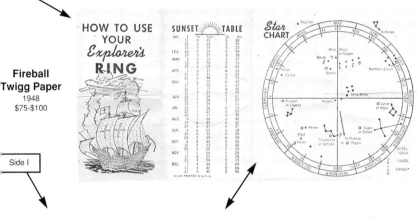

HOW TO USE YOUR EXPLORER'S RING

COMPASS: (All boys and girls)

The compass in your Explorer's Ring is a *magnetic* compass — just the same as Columbus used and sea captains and airplane pilots are still using. When you hold the ring level, the needle points to *magnetic* North. By turning the ring so that N is under the point of the needle, you can determine any other direction. You must be careful not to have any magnetic metal such as iron or steel near the compass when you are using it, or the needle will be deflected from *magnetic* north. You will have to get off your bicycle to read it accurately. And you will have to hold it away from your pocket knife, keys, or other iron and steel.

(High school boys and girls)

Actually, there is a difference between *magnetic* north and *true* north, although in some areas it is so small that you don't have to pay any attention to it. That difference is known as *variation* and, if it is big, must be compensated for in order to get strict accuracy. Sea captains and pilots do it, and so must you. It is not hard to compensate for variation, in fact it is fun.

On the back of this sheet you will find a VARIATION MAP. In some places it is blank. If you live in

· 1 ·

such a locality, there is not enough variation for you to worry about. But in other places where the variation is greater the map will be marked W for West or E for East.

If the *variation* for your locality is listed as W, that means that *magnetic north* is slightly to the left or west of *true north*. So you turn the ring so the N is slightly to the right of the point of the needle. Then the N is more precisely at true north, the E at true east, and so on. In case the *variation* is East, turn the ring so the N is slightly to the left of the needle. If no *variation* is given, put the N right under the needle.

SUN WATCH: (All boys and girls)

Turn your Explorer's Ring so that N is under the point of the needle. Make sure you are holding it so the sun can fall on it. Then see where the shadow from the little white vane falls. This will tell you the approximate time according to the sun.

(High school boys and girls)

If you allow for the *variation* in your locality as explained above, the time will be more accurate.

However, all sun dials and sun watches tell the time according to *the sun*. This is called solar time. The kind of time we normally use in the United States is Civil Time

· 2 ·

1995   **123**   OVERSTREET PREMIUM RING PRICE GUIDE

HURRY! HURRY! KIDS! GET FIREBALL'S EXPLORER'S RING

THAT REALLY TELLS TIME!

REAL MAGNETIC COMPASS THAT GLOWS in the DARK!
GENUINE SUNWATCH THAT TELLS YOU THE TIME!

PROTECTED BY PLASTIC DOME JUST LIKE NAVIGATOR'S BUBBLE ON BIG PLANES.

RICH! MODERN! BEAUTIFUL!

YOU CAN'T BUY THIS RING ANYWHERE ELSE. IF YOU COULD IT WOULD COST A LOT MORE.

PLATED WITH BEAUTIFUL, EXPENSIVE, SHINING RHODIUM. WILL NOT TARNISH OR CORRODE!

FITS ANY FINGER!

ONLY 25¢

EASY TO GET
EASY TO USE
Send 25¢ and one box top from any Post cereal. Print your name and address. We'll rush your ring. Full directions with every ring. Price includes handling charge, postage, and any applicable Federal tax.

Fireball Twigg, Dept. 40, Box 60
Battle Creek, Michigan
Here is my quarter and my box top. Rush one Explorer's Ring to:

Name _____
Street and No. _____
Town _____

WOW! What a ring! It's handsome ... and valuable. Made from expensive plastic acetate and real rhodium!

The Explorer's Ring is useful, too ... a real compass and a real sun dial. Any boy or girl right up through high school

will find it entertaining and instructive. Can be used to predict the time of sunset and to help identify the stars. Many other uses. Full directions in booklet. Send for it today.

Offer void in any state, locality or municipality where prohibited, taxed or otherwise restricted. *Patent Pending

Post's GRAPE-NUTS WHEAT MEAL   Post's GRAPE-NUTS FLAKES   Post's GRAPE NUTS

Copyright 1948, General Foods Corp.

YAHOO! HERE IT IS!

YOUR EXPLORER'S RING THAT TELLS TIME

TELL YOUR FRIENDS HOW TO GET THIS SENSATIONAL RING!
USE THIS HANDY COUPON.

FIREBALL TWIGG, P. O. Box 60, Battle Creek, Mich.
Please send me the following number of "THE EXPLORER'S RING" that tells time:
1 — 2 — 3 — 4 — 5 — 6 — 7 — 8 (Circle number desired)
I enclose 25c and one box top* for each EXPLORER'S RING.
*Box top from either Post's Grape-Nuts, Post's Grape-Nuts Flakes, Post's Grape-Nuts Wheat Meal.

NAME_____
ADDRESS_____
CITY_____ STATE_____
This offer void in any state or municipality where prohibited, taxed, or otherwise restricted. Offer good only in U. S. A., and its territorial possessions. Offer expires Sept. 15, 1948.

Sundial tells time

lintstones-Bam Bam
1960 (metal, cloisonne)
$20-$40

Flintstones-Fred
1960s (small, metal cloisonne)
$20-$40

Flintstones-Fred
1960s(metal cloisonne)
$20-$40

Flintstones-Barney
Rubble (metal cloisonne)
$20-$40

Flintstones-Fred
1960s (metal, cloisonne)
$20-$40

Flintstones-Pebbles
1960s (metal cloisonne)
$20-$40

Flintstones-Betty
1960s (plastic)(blue over white)
$20-$40

Flintstones-Dino
1960s (metal, cloisonne)
$20-$40

Flintstones-Barney
1966 (set of 6)(plastic)

Flintstones-Betty
1966 (set of 6)(plastic)

Flintstones-Pebbles
1966 (set of 6)(plastic)

Flintstones-Dino
1966 (set of 6)(plastic)

Flintstones
1966 (4 rings on card)(vending machine)
(plastic(figures snap on base)
$450 complete

Flintstones-Fred
1966 (set of 6)(plastic)

Flintstones, Wilma
1966 (set of 6)(plastic)
$65-$80 ea.

Flying Saucer
(see Capt. Video, Quisp &
Wheaties)

Flying Tigers
(see Roger Wilco)

#201—FOOTBALL RING
A heavy golden finished Football ring you'll be proud to wear. Send only 3 Touchdown wrappers and 15¢ to:
TOUCHDOWN, P.O. Box 239
New York 8, N. Y.
(Not valid where contrary to State laws)
Offer expires 1/31/49 ©Bowman Gum, Inc., 1948

Football
1948 (Bowman gum)(prices
vary on gum cards)
ring only - $100-$300

Foghorn Leghorn
(see Looney Tunes)

Football Flicker
1970s (metal (Hong Kong)
$5-$10

Florida Orange Bird
1970 (metal cloisonne)
$20-$40

Fonz
1970s (metal)(photo)
$50-$125

Ford PP&K Flicker
1960s
$2-$5

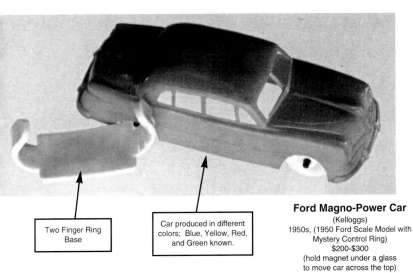

Two Finger Ring
Base

Car produced in different
colors; Blue, Yellow, Red,
and Green known.

Ford Magno-Power Car
(Kelloggs)
1950s, (1950 Ford Scale Model with
Mystery Control Ring)
$200-$300
(hold magnet under a glass
to move car across the top)

Boys! Girls!

Here it is! Your REAL ACTION MAGNO-POWER '50 Ford SCALE MODEL

with **MYSTERY CONTROL RING**

TURN QUICK

It's Amazing! Thrill your friends and family!

HERE'S HOW TO MAKE CAR OPERATE!

It's the magnetic "Two Finger" ring control that does the trick! Adjust plastic ring under middle two fingers and keep magnet hidden in your palm.

Hold hand over 1950 miniature Ford model. Watch it speed forward—backward! Secret magnets will make car move! One end of magnet attracts; other end repels. IMPORTANT: Hold ring *lengthwise* over car. Try holding hand over both ends of car. See which end works better for you. Note: Practice alone for a few minutes before showing car to friends. Don't get ring too close or too far from car.

YOU'LL "GO FOR" PEP, TOO!

Get hep to whole-wheat goodness! Ask Mom to *keep on* serving Kellogg's PEP! Every bowlful a tempting treat. Ummmmmmm! Rich, malty, nut-brown flakes, ready to eat. So nourishing, too! Delicious served with milk, sugar, and fruit. Each spoonful comes up crisp and crunchy because PEP is Kellogg-fresh.

Keep your eye on PEP! There's something new in every package! More fun! Laughs! Eye-popping thrills! Ask Mom to order plenty of PEP!

Kellogg's PEP WHOLE WHEAT FLAKES

For Sunshine Vitamin **D** and Energy Vitamin **B₁**

Ford Magno-Power Car Paper
(Complete) 1950
$75-$100

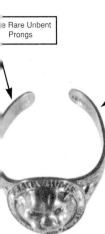

Frank Buck Black Leopard
(bronze), 1938 (scarce)
(note unbent prongs)
Good - $700
Fine - $1400
Near Mint - $2800

Frank Buck Movie
(Bring 'Em Back Alive)
1930s (metal)
$100-$200

ank Buck Black Leopard
(silver metal), 1938
Good - $450
Fine - $900
Near Mint - $1800

Frank Sinatra
(see Real Photo)

Frankenberry
(See Boo Berry & Count Chocula)

Frank Buck World's Fair
N.Y., 1939 (rare)(metal)
Good - $1125
Fine - $2250
Near Mint - $4500

**Frank Buck
Ivory Initial**
1940s (real ivory)
$150-$350

Frankenberry Flicker
Looking in mirror, $40-$75

Frankenberry Flicker
Playing drum, $40-$75

Frankenbery
Dancing

Frankenberry Flickers
1980s (3 in set)(plastic)
$40-$75 ea.

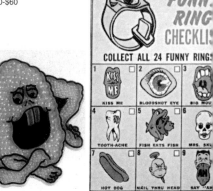

Freakies Figural
1978 (green plastic)(United Features)
$30-$60

Top pops open to reveal
secret compartment

**Frankenberry Secret
Compartment**
(plastic) (chocolate color)
1980s
$75-$150

Freakies
1978 (orange plastic)
(Universal Feat.)
$40-$100

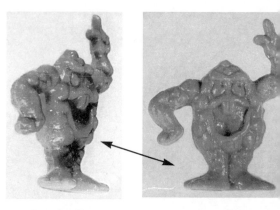

FUNN.
RING
CHECKLI!

COLLECT ALL 24 FUNNY RING!

Frankenstein
1980s (metal cloisonne)(Universxal)
$10-$20

Frankenstein (see Universal Monsters)

Frito Bandito
(plastic) (in platic bag)
1970s $50-$100

Funny Rings (24 set), **Top**
(cardboard) (checklist shown
above), 1966 ($750-$1500) (se
or $30-$60 ea.

FUNNY RING 1

(see previous page for prices)

FUNNY RING 5

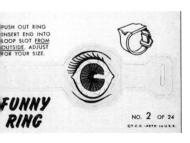

FUNNY RING 2

FUNNY RING 6

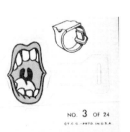

FUNNY RING 3

FUNNY RING 7

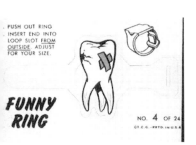

FUNNY RING 4

FUNNY RING 8

1. PUSH OUT RING
2. INSERT END INTO LOOP SLOT FROM OUTSIDE. ADJUST FOR YOUR SIZE.

FUNNY RING

NO. 9 OF 24
C.T.C.G.—PRTD. IN U.S.A.

FUNNY RING 9

1. PUSH OUT RING
2. INSERT END INTO LOOP SLOT FROM OUTSIDE. ADJUST FOR YOUR SIZE.

FUNNY RING

IF YOU CAN READ THIS —SCRAM!

NO. 13 OF

C.T.C.G.—PRTD. IN

FUNNY RING 13

(see next page for prices)

1. PUSH OUT RING
2. INSERT END INTO LOOP SLOT FROM OUTSIDE. ADJUST FOR YOUR SIZE.

FUNNY RING

NO. 10 OF 24
C.T.C.G.—PRTD. IN U.S.A.

FUNNY RING 10

1. PUSH OUT RING
2. INSERT END INTO LOOP SLOT FROM OUTSIDE. ADJUST FOR YOUR SIZE.

NUTS TO YOU

FUNNY RING

NO. 14 OF
C.T.C.G.—PRTD. IN

FUNNY RING 14

1. PUSH OUT RING
2. INSERT END INTO LOOP SLOT FROM OUTSIDE. ADJUST FOR YOUR SIZE.

FUNNY RING

NO. 11 OF 24
C.T.C.G.—PRTD. IN U.S.A.

FUNNY RING 11

1. PUSH OUT RING
2. INSERT END INTO LOOP SLOT FROM OUTSIDE. ADJUST FOR YOUR SIZE.

GET LOST

FUNNY RING

NO. 15 OF
C.T.C.G.—PRTD. IN U

FUNNY RING 15

1. PUSH OUT RING
2. INSERT END INTO LOOP SLOT FROM OUTSIDE. ADJUST FOR YOUR SIZE.

FUNNY RING

NO. 12 OF 24
C.T.C.G.—PRTD. IN U.S.A.

FUNNY RING 12

1. PUSH OUT RING
2. INSERT END INTO LOOP SLOT FROM OUTSIDE. ADJUST FOR YOUR SIZE.

YOU FINK

FUNNY RING

NO. 16 OF
C.T.C.G.—PRTD. IN

FUNNY RING 16

1. PUSH OUT RING
2. INSERT END INTO LOOP SLOT FROM OUTSIDE. ADJUST FOR YOUR SIZE.

FUNNY RING

NO. 23 OF 24
© T.C.G.—PRTD. IN U.S.A.

FUNNY RING 17

1. PUSH OUT RING
2. INSERT END INTO LOOP SLOT FROM OUTSIDE. ADJUST FOR YOUR SIZE.

FUNNY RING

NO. 17 OF 24
© T.C.G.—PRTD. IN U.S.A.

FUNNY RING 21

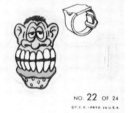

1. PUSH OUT RING
2. INSERT END INTO LOOP SLOT FROM OUTSIDE. ADJUST FOR YOUR SIZE.

FUNNY RING

NO. 22 OF 24
© T.C.G.—PRTD. IN U.S.A.

FUNNY RING 18

1. PUSH OUT RING
2. INSERT END INTO LOOP SLOT FROM OUTSIDE. ADJUST FOR YOUR SIZE.

FUNNY RING

NO. 21 OF 24
© T.C.G.—PRTD. IN U.S.A.

FUNNY RING 22

1. PUSH OUT RING
2. INSERT END INTO LOOP SLOT FROM OUTSIDE. ADJUST FOR YOUR SIZE.

FUNNY RING

NO. 19 OF 24
© T.C.G.—PRTD. IN U.S.A.

FUNNY RING 19

1. PUSH OUT RING
2. INSERT END INTO LOOP SLOT FROM OUTSIDE. ADJUST FOR YOUR SIZE.

FUNNY RING

NO. 18 OF 24
© T.C.G.—PRTD. IN U.S.A.

FUNNY RING 23

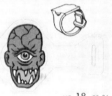

1. PUSH OUT RING
2. INSERT END INTO LOOP SLOT FROM OUTSIDE. ADJUST FOR YOUR SIZE.

FUNNY RING

NO. 20 OF 24
© T.C.G.—PRTD. IN U.S.A.

FUNNY RING 24

1. PUSH OUT RING
2. INSERT END INTO LOOP SLOT FROM OUTSIDE. ADJUST FOR YOUR SIZE.

FUNNY RING

NO. 24 OF 24
© T.C.G.—PRTD. IN U.S.A.

FUNNY RING 20

↑ **Funny Ring**
1966 (set of 24)
$30-$60 ea.

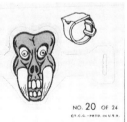

Fuzzy Head
1980s
$2-$4

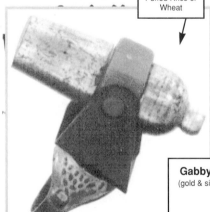

Gabby Hayes Cannon
(gold & silver versions), Quaker,
1951
$100-$250

Gabby Hayes Shooting Cannon paper
1951 (metal/plastic)
$75-$100

Gabby Hayes
(see Real Photos)

Game Ring
1940s
$50-$150

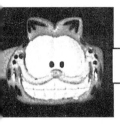

Garfield
1978 (plastic)
$8-$15

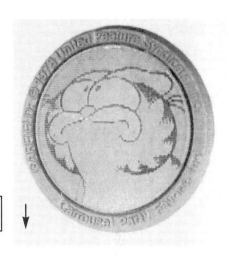

Garfield Flicker (2)
Content looking Garfield with eyes shut to
wided eyed surprized looking Garfield.

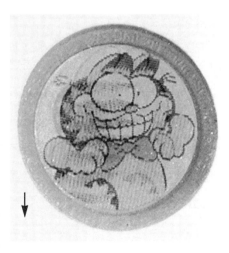

Garfield Flicker (3)
Round Green rings with smiling
Garfield putting toothpaste on brush
to tube of paste exploding toothpaste all over him.

Garfield Flicker (3)
1978 (plastic)(large size)
(3 in set)(United Features Synd.)
$5-$10 ea.

Garfield Flicker (1)
Garfield small mouth to Garfield
large mouth (both versions shown)

Gary Cooper (see Real Photo)

ANOTHER GENE AUTRY SPECIAL— THE AMERICAN EAGLE RING!

This spectacular ring is yours FREE if you subscribe now to Gene Autry Comics. It's shiny golden color and the American Eagle emblazoned under a transparent setting is sure to make this ring a favorite of boys and girls everywhere. Be the first among your friends to own one. Subscribe now to Gene Autry Comics and receive this handsome ring as our FREE gift.

Think what fun it will be to have your copy of Gene Autry comics delivered right to your home each month! You'll be sure of getting every issue and receive this handsome ring FREE also. And you save money . . . 12 adventure-filled issues of Gene Autry comics costs just $1.

If you are already a subscriber you can still take advantage of this great FREE offer because we'll send you your ring now and start your new subscription when your present one expires.

CUT ON DOTTED LINE. PLEASE PRINT PLAINLY.

SUBSCRIPTION RATES: ☐ 1 year-12 issues $1.00
☐ 2 yrs.-24 issues $1.85 ☐ 3 yrs.-36 issues $2.70
Canada: ☐ 1 yr. $1.20; ☐ 2 yrs. $2.00; ☐ 3 yrs. $3.00

A PLEDGE DELL COMIC TO PARENTS

The Dell Trademark is, and always has been, a positive guarantee that the comic magazine bearing it contains only clean and wholesome juvenile entertainment. The Dell code eliminates entirely, rather than regulates, objectionable material. That's why when your child buys a Dell Comic you can be sure it contains only good fun. "DELL COMICS ARE GOOD COMICS" is our credo and constant goal.

Mail To: DELL PUBLISHING CO., INC. DEPT. 5GA
10 W. 33rd St., New York 1, N. Y.

Please enter subscription to Gene Autry Comics. Include special offer of Free American Eagle Ring and Dell Comics Club Membership Certificate.

Name .... Age ....

St. and No. ....

City ....

I am enclosing re.........
payment.
  (If this is a gift su...........
          addition........
        ENCLOSE G.........

Donor's Name ....

St. and No. ....

City ....

Gene Autry Eagle Paper
Ad From Gene Autry Comics #99, May 1955
(price based on value of comic book)(see
the Overstreet Comic Book Price Guide)

Gene Autry Eagle
(Gene Autry Dell comic book ad
premium), 1955 (scarce)
$250-$500

Gene Autry Face
(copper w/enamel coating)
1950s
$75-$150

Gene Autry Flag
1950s, (Dell, gold
& silver versions)
$100-$200

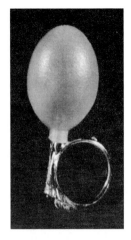

Genie Squirt
Ring, 1990s
$2-$4

Gene Autry Face
(copper) 1950s
$75-$150

Gene Autry Nail
on Card, 1950 (metal)
(also see Tom Mix Nail)
ring only $20-$40
with card - $200

Gene Autry Photo
(see Real Photos)

Gerber Baby Food
1940s (metal)
$25-$75

Gene Autry Face
(aluminum w/gold face) 1950s
$75-$150

Gene Kelly
(see Movie Star photo)

Gene Tunney
(plastic), 1950s (Kelloggs)
$20-$40

Gene Autry Face
(silver), 1950s
$75-$150

Ghost Busters
(movie) 1992 (metal cloisonne)
$2-$4

G.I. Joe® Command Rings are worn by Joe™ and Cobra™ forces to signify their combat speciality. Never before have these rings been available to you. Now, you can collect all 8 and show your friends that you're a member of the elite G.I. Joe Forces!

COLLECT ALL 8

AIRBORNE ARTILLERY FORCE

ARCTIC FORCE INFANTRY S.E.A.L.

SHUTTLE CREW T.A.R.G.A.T. TANK CORPS

G.I. Joe Paper
1980s
$10-$20

G. I. Joe Artic
1980s, $5-$10

G.I. Joe Artillery
1980s, $5-$10

G.I. Joe Seal
1980s, $5-$10

G.I. Joe Shuttle
1980s, $5-$10

G.I. Joe Target
1980s, $5-$10

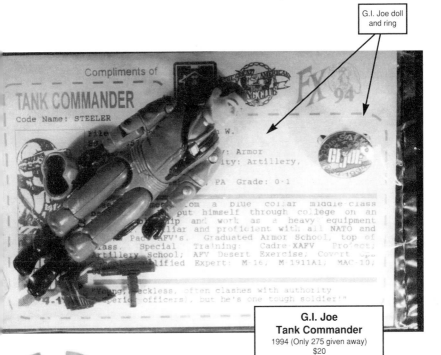

Compliments of

TANK COMMANDER
Code Name: STEELER

FX 94

y: Armor
ty: Artillery,

PA Grade: O-1

om a blue collar middle-class
put himself through college on an
and work as a heavy equipment
iliar and proficient with all NATO and
Pa FV's. Graduated Armor School, top of
ass. Special Training: Cadre XAFV Project;
rtillery School; AFV Desert Exercise, Covert
lified Expert: M-16, M-1911A1, MAC-10;

ong, ckless, often clashes with authority
peri officers), but he's one tough soldier!"

**G.I. Joe
Tank Commander**
1994 (Only 275 given away)
$20

G.I. Joe Tank
1980s
$5-$10

G.I. Joe
1982 (came on card display
with pinback)(metal)
on card - $100
ring only - $40-$75

G.I. Joe Special Forces
1994
Blue stone - $250, Black stone - $400

G.I. Joe Coin
1964-1994 (30th salute)
1994
Gold - $400
Silver - $200
Bronze - $100

G-Men (name in G)
1930s (metal)
$20-$50

**Goudy Gum
Cowboy Boot**
(see cowboy boot)

**Goudy Gum
Cowboy Hat**
(see cowboy hat)

Goudy Gum Indian
(see Indian)

Granger, Farley
(see Movie Star Photo)

Giant (Circus)
1940s (scarce)
$50-$100

G-Men (name below G)
1930s (metal)
$20-$60

Green Beret
(movie), 1970s
$10-$20

Black
color

Gold color
(scarce)

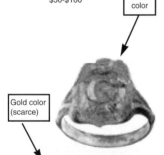

Golden Nugget Cave
(casino), 1950s (rare(less than
10 known)(see Straight
Arrow Nugget)
$300-$500

G-Man Club
1930s (gum ball)(black & gold
versions)
$2-$5

Goofy
3D figure (in color)
$50-$100

Green Giant
1980s (rubber)
$25-$50

Green Hornet Flicker (1)
"The Green Hornet" to small silhouette of the Green Hornet firing hornet gun next to car.

Green Hornet Flicker (5)
Face of Britt Reid to face of the Green Hornet.

Green Hornet Flicker (10)
Picure of a couple kissing to black beauty driving thru a wall.

Green Hornet Flicker (2)
Picture of A Green Hornet to face of the Green Hornet with mask.

Green Hornet Flicker (6)
Full figure of Kato as butler to full figure Kato in front of car.

Green Hornet Flicker (11)
Hornet sting weapons to "Sting".

Green Hornet Flicker (3)
"Green Hornet Action ring" to full figure of the green hornet holding sting gun.

Green Hornet Flicker(7)
Full figure of the Green Hornet running from car with sting gun to Hornet rescuing a woman.

Green Hornet Flicker (12)
"Hornet Gun" to a guy getting gassed.

Green Hornet Flicker
1960s (silver)(set of 12)
$10-$20 ea.

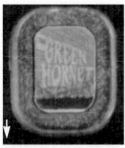

Green Hornet Flicker (1)

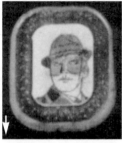

Green Hornet Flicker (2)

Green Hornet Flicker (3)

Green Hornet Flicker (4)

Green Hornet Flicker (5)

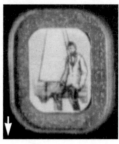

Green Hornet Flicker (6)

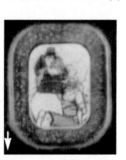

Green Hornet Flicker (7)

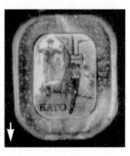

Green Hornet Flicker (8)

Green Hornet Flicker

Green Hornet Flicker

Green Hornet Flicker (

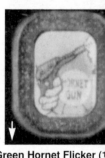

Green Hornet Flicker (1

↑ Green Hornet Flicker
1960s (set of 12)(plastic)(blue ba
$8-$15 ea.

Green Hornet
(plastic), 1930s (rare)(only 10 known)
Good - $550
Fine - $1100
Near Mint -$2200

Green Hornet Seal
1966
$10-$20

Green Hornet Stamp
1960s (plastic)
$15-$30

Green Hornet
1960s (plastic)
$8-$15

Metal top swivels
open to reveal secret
compartment

(Also see Knights Of
Columbus which
uses same ring
base

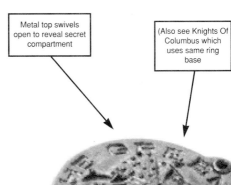

**Green
Hornet**
1970s (plastic)
$2-$4

Glow-in-
dark secret
compartment

Green Hornet
Rubber, 1966
$5-$10

Green Hornet Seal
(Secret Compartment),
General Mills, 1947, (Base glows-in-dark)
Good - $400
Fine - $800
Near Mint - $1200

NOTICE!

HOW TO SIGNAL WITH THIS GREEN HORNET RING

1. Activate the Secret Signal Radiator by sliding back shutter and exposing to strong light. For instance, hold close to electric light bulb for a few seconds.

2. When the Secret Signal Radiator is activated, use your ring for signaling at night. Remember— the darker the night, the better it works. Signal by moving the swinging shutter back and forth according to your own secret code. It's easy to make a code that only you and your friends will understand by combining different long and short flashes.

3. This ring designed only for short-range, under-cover communication. Do not attempt to use for signaling more than 25 feet.

HOW TO LEAVE GREEN HORNET SEAL

To leave official seal of the Green Hornet, follow these easy instructions:

Select some soft material, such as paper and press it down on top of ring. Do not press ring down on soft material for pressing too hard in this manner may damage swinging shutter mechanism.

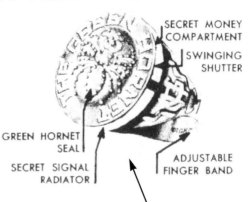

SECRET MONEY COMPARTMENT

SWINGING SHUTTER

GREEN HORNET SEAL

SECRET SIGNAL RADIATOR

ADJUSTABLE FINGER BAND

Green Hornet Seal Paper
1947 (complete)
$100-$150

SPECIAL "GOOD TURN" COUPON GIVE IT TO A FRIEND

When you signal with this ring to your friends, you'll want them to signal back. So they'll need an Official Green Hornet Night Signaling Ring, too.

Let your friends use this coupon to send for this amazing ring. It will help speed delivery.

- -

FILL OUT AND MAIL AT ONCE TO:

ADDRESS: General Mills, Inc., Dept. 536
623 Marquette Ave., Minneapolis 2, Minn.

GREEN HORNET: I am enclosing 15c and the words "Model City" cut from the Betty Crocker Cereal Tray. Please send me an Official Green Hornet Night Signaling Ring. *Please do not send stamps.*

_____
NAME (Print Plainly)

_____
ADDRESS

TOWN   ZONE   STATE
A3963

Green Lantern Glow-in-dark
1992 DC Comic giveaway
$2

Note: Marty Nodell, creator of Green Lantern has given away examples of this ring autographed. $4 ea.

FULLY POSEABLE FIGURE WITH ITS
OWN UNIQUE ACTION FEATURE.

AGES 5 AND

DC COMICS SUPER HEROES

GREEN LANTERN

WITH
**WATER
JET
RING**

Green Lantern Water Jet
(squirt), 1980s
(on card) $12-$24
(ring only), $8-$16

Gremlin
1980s (metal cloisonne)
$8-$15

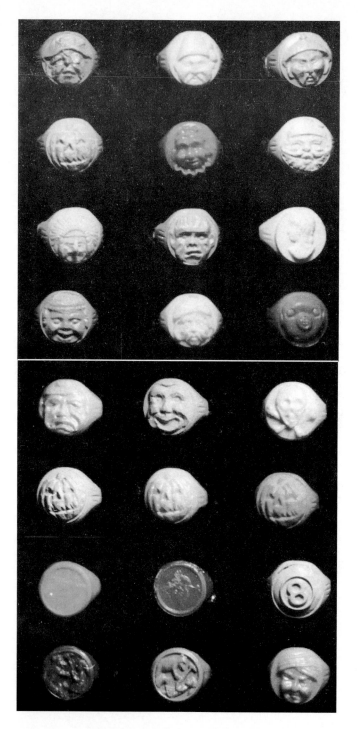

Gum ball set
1960s (18 in set)
$4 each

Gumby (7 diff.)
1980s (plastic)
$3-$6 ea.

Gumby (set with paper) (7 diff.)
1980s
$50 set

Hagar The Horrible
1993 (silver metal)(Staber)
silver (46 made) - $150
Gold (12 made) - $600

Halloween packaged set of 24 rings
1990s, $4 in package

Hans (see Post Tin)

Have Gun Will Travel
(Paladin)(plastic, gold base)
$15-$25

Henry The Chicken Hawk
(see Looney Tunes)

Hansel and Gretel
1992 (secret compartment)
(red plastic)
$20-$40

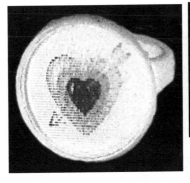

Hiawatha Flicker
(1970s (Looney Tunes)
(modern "v" base)
$2-$5

Hardy Boys
1960s
$25-$50

Heart-Arrow Flicker
1960s (plastic)(Cupid)(see Valentine)
$3-$6

Hills Brothers
(see Captain Bill)

Harold Teen (see Post Tin)

Heart Throbs Flicker
1970s (silver base)
$2-$5

Have Gun Will Travel
(Paladin) (White & black top
versions) (T.V.), 1960s
Ring only - $25-$50
on card - $75

Henry (see Post Tin)

Holly Hobby
1970s (metal cloisonne)
$25-$50

HOPPY'S DICTIONARY
OF WESTERN
HORSES

MUSTANG

BRONCO

QUARTER HORSE

PINTO OR PIEBALD

© Wm. Boyd

PALOMINO

Coupon from Delicia cone cups needed to order Hopalong Cassidy Bar 20 ring

Ring listing from back of above coupon

HOPALONG CASSIDY
ADJUSTABLE RING & BADGE

Wear Hoppy's official badge and ring to identify yourself as a real range rider. Both in handsome silver colored finish embossed with Hoppy's picture. Ring adjustable to any size. Mail 2 Box Top Coupons and 25c in coin to H. C. Badge & Ring Dept.

Hopalong Cassidy Bar 20 paper
1950s, $50-$60

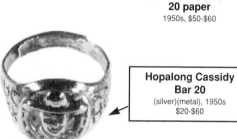

Hopalong Cassidy Bar 20
(silver)(metal), 1950s
$20-$60

Hat fits over compass base

Hoover/Wilson Flicker
1960s (metal)(Hong Kong)
$20-$35

Hopalong Cassidy Bar 20
(brass), 1950s
$20-$60

Hopalong Cassidy Compass/Hat (metal)
1950s, $100-$200

Hopalong Cassidy Steer Head
ring/slide, 1950s (rare)
(mouth opens so teeth can
punch brand on inserted paper)
$150-$300

Hopalong Cassidy
Photo (William Boyd)
(see Real Photos)

Horror Ring
Paper
1950s (vending
machine paper)(in
color)(rare)
$15-$25

ITEM NO. 52/482

Horror Rings Boxed Set
(rings different than boxed set on next page)
1950s - $140 set

Horror rings boxed set
1950s,(ring design different than other
boxed set)
$160 set

Horseshoe (see Tiger Eye)

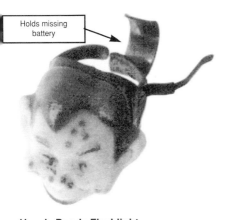

Holds missing battery

Howdy Doody Flashlight
1950s
$75-$200 complete w/battery

Flubadub Flicker

(see next page for prices)

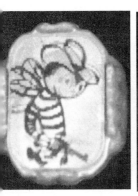

Buffalo Bee Flicker

Chief Thunderthud Flicker

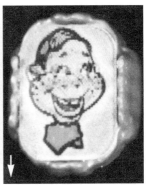

Howdy Doody Flicker

Buffalo Bob Flicker

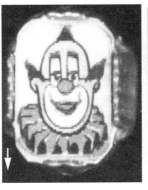

Clarabelle Flicker

Mr. Bluster Flicker

Princess

Howdy Doody Flicker
1950s (set of 8)(Nabisco Rice
Honeys cereal premium)
$15-$30 ea.

Howdy Doody Jack in Box
1950s (rare) (red & yellow
plastic) (two color versions exist)
Good - $1735
Fine - $3470
Near Mint - $5200

Howdy Raised Face
(silver base), 1950s
$75-$150

Howdy Doody Raise
Face (white base), 1950s
$75-$150

Howdy Doody
1976 (metal/plastic)
$50-$100

**Howdy Doody/Poll
Parrot Flicker**
(showing Poll Parrot)(see price
below)

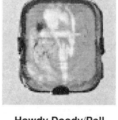

**Howdy Doody Glow
Photo,** 1950s
$75-$150

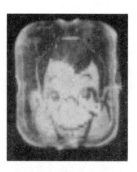

**Howdy Doody/ Poll
Parrot Flicker**
1950s (showing Howdy Doody)
(Thick top lens held on by four prongs)
$50-$100

Howdy Doody /Poll Parrot
Flicker, 1950s (scarce)(blue or ora
bases)(showing Poll Parrot & Howd
$300-$600

Howdy Doody Insert
(red base), 1950s
$75-$150

Howie Wing Weather
1940s (scarce)(metal)
$250-$500

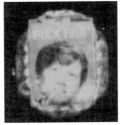

Huckleberry Hound
(aluminum, 1960s)
$15-$30

**H.R. Puf'n Stuf
(Cling & Clang)**

Huck Finn Flicker
1950s (shows both images)
$10-$20

Huckleberry Hound (see
Baba Looey, Dixie & Quick Draw
McGraw)

Huckleberry Hound Club
1960s
$30-$100

**H.R. Puf'n Stuf
(Puff 'n Stuff)**

**H.R. Puf'n Stuf
(Witchiepoo)**

H.R. Puf 'n Stuf
(7 diff.), 1970s
$20-$40 ea.

Humpty Dumpty
1970s (plastic)(red over white)
$5 - $10

Incredible Hulk
1980s(metal)(also see Captain
America (Marvel Ent. Group)(in colo
$50-$100

Huskies Club
(cereal), 1936 (rare)(metal)
$250-$500

Hush Puppies Flicker
"Hush Puppies" picture of the
dog to "casual shoes" picture
of dog looking other way.
1960s
$15-$30

Initial (generic)
1950s, $5-$10

Indian, Goudy Gum
1940s (metal)(also see Chief Wah
$75-$150

Initial Ring
1940's (metal)(premium)(scarce)
$100-$200

Indian Boy Flicker
Indian boy paddling a canoe
1960s, $2

Ice Maiden Magnet
1990s
$3-$6

Indian
1940s (gumball)(metal)
$20-$40

Inspector (see Post Tir

Ingersoll

1948 card display (10 rings)(individual rings are listed and priced under the character names)
complete - $2000

FOLLOW JACK ARMSTRONG'S TRAINING RULES

Here's the special training program designed for young athletes and recommended by nationally famous coaches and players. Follow these rules regularly and you're helping yourself to deliver better performance at your favorite sports.

1. Get plenty of fresh air, sleep and exercise every day. These are basic training requirements needed to help put you in condition for fast, strenuous play.

2. Make a friend of soap and water. Dirt breeds germs, and germs can very easily undermine an athlete's condition. Good health is vital to success in sports.

3. Eat a "Breakfast of Champions" every morning! Treat yourself to a big bowlful of nourishing whole wheat, Wheaties, with lots of milk and fruit. Probably more great athletes eat this training breakfast than any other dish of its kind.

YOURS! THIS MYSTERIOUS RING THAT GLOWS IN THE DARK!

Only 10c and a Wheaties box top bring you a genuine "Mystic Dragon's Eye" finger ring. Send coupon now!

It's weird! It's baffling! This beautiful finger ring of ivory-like plastic has the strange power of shining in darkness with a luminous glow that startles all who see it. Gleams at night like the eye of a jungle cat! Ring is embossed with crocodile figures; fitted with cross-tenite center decoration, adjustable to fit any finger. Be the first in your neighborhood to own one. Mail coupon at once! Offer good only while present supplies last.

MAIL THIS COUPON TODAY

WHEATIES
Department 527
Minneapolis, Minnesota

Send me .... "Mystic Dragon's Eye" finger rings for which
I enclose .... cents and .... Wheaties box tops. (Send 10c and one Wheaties box top for each ring you want.)

Name ....
Street ....
Town .... State ....

Breakfast of Champions
"WITH MILK OR CREAM AND SUGAR OR FRUIT"

IMPORTAN

HOW TO "CHARGE" YOUR LUMIN DRAGON'S EYE RING TO MAKE GLOW IN THE DARK!

Hold your dragon's eye ring up clos a lighted electric bulb for one half m ute or more. This "charges" your d on's eye ring so it will glow in the d —the longer you hold your ring to light, the brighter and longer it will glow. You may "charge" ring this way as often as you wish. You can also "charge" y dragon's eye ring by holding it in the sunlight. *But be sure do not expose your ring to the direct rays of the sun for long a time!*

IF YOU WANT TO MAKE YOUR RING LARGER: (1) P it in hot water (not boiling) for about five minutes. (2) T it from the water and put it on your finger, bending it to right size. (3) When you have bent it so it fits, put it in water for a minute. (4) Your ring should now fit perfectly

(Special Order Blank on other side)

Jack Armstrong Dragon's Eye Paper
1940s (rare), $100-$150

Green stone (base glows in dark)

Jack Armstrong Dragon's Eye
1940s (green stone)(also see Buck Rogers Rin of Saturn & Shadow Carey Salt)
$300-$1000

Jack Armstrong Baseball Centennial
(1839 - 1939) 1939 (metal)(rare)
$325-$625

JACK ARMSTRONG'S SECRET WHISTLE CODE

INSTRUCTIONS

One Whistle . . . . (Short) Attention

Two Whistles . . . . (Short) Be on guard for trouble

Three Whistles . . . . . . (One long, two short) In danger, come at once

Four Whistles . . . . . . (Short) We're being watched

Two Whistles . . . . . . (Two Long) Important news — meet me at once

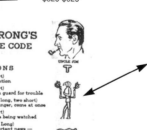

Jack Armstrong Egyptian Whistle Paper
1940s, (beware of repro paper), $40-$50

Jack Armstrong Egyptian Whistle
1940s (metal)(gold color)
(also see Tom Mix Musical)
$40-$125

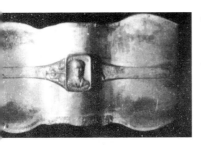

Jack Armstrong Lead Proof
1939 (Ring was never issued)
$1500

Jack Benny Photo
(see Real Photos)

Jack Kramer
(plastic,orange top,
brown base)
& (blue top, green
base), 1950s
$20-$40

Jackie Gleason Photo (See Real Photos)

Jackie Kennedy Photo (See Real Photos)

James Bond
(see Agent 007)

Jasmine
(see Aladdin)

Jerry's Restaurants Flicker
"Jerry's Restaurants" to cartoon figure of
a chef.
1960s, $10-$20

Jesus Flicker
1970s
$10-$20

Jet Plane (See Super Jet)

Jetsons, Judy
1980s (metal cloisonne)
$10-$25

Jiggs (see Post Tin)

Jimminy Crickett
1960s (aluminum)
$20-$35

Jimminy Crickett
1960s
(plastic)(red over
white)
$15-$25

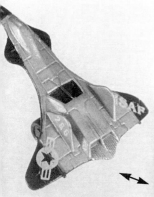

Jet Fighter
1978 (with launching base)(plastic)
$5-$10

Jimmy Allen Flying
Club, 1930s
$50-$100

Jimmy Durante Photo
(see Real Photos)

Jinx (Hanna-Barbera)
1960s (aluminum)(also see Dixie)
$15-$30

Joanne Dru
1950s
$10-$20

Joe Dimaggio club
1940s
$200-$375

Joe E. Brown
1940s
$50-$100

Joe Louis Face
1940s (rare) (nickel metal)
$1000-$2500

Joe Louis Figural
1940s (scarce) Metal (2 color
variations)
$500-$1000

Joe Louis Photo
(see Real Photos)

Joe Penner Face Puzzle
1940s (rare)(radio)(less than 10 known)
$300-$600

Joel McCrae
(see Real Photo)

John F. Kennedy Flicker
1960s (gold metal base)(oval)
$10-$20

John F. Kennedy Flicker
1960s (gold metal base)
$10-$20

John F. Kennedy Flicker
John F. Kennedy 35th president
1917-1963 picture of American
Flag to face of JFK.
1960s, $10-$20

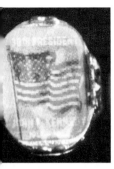

nn F. Kennedy Flicker
1960s (oval)
$10-$20

hn F. Kennedy Photo
(see Real Photos)

John Wayne Photo
Movie Star Photo & Real Photo))

Junior Pilot
1955 (American Airlines)
$10-$25

King Comics, Blondie

Junior Stewardess
(American Airlines)
1955, $10-$25

Kangaroo (see Looney Tunes)

King Comics, Captain

**Jungle Jim's
Playland Ring**
1980's
$2-$4

Kewpie
1940s (metal)
$75-$150

King Comics, Felix

Junior Fire Marshal
1950s
$10-$25

**Kill the Jinx Good Luck
Signet Ring,** 1929 (metal)
(sold in Johnson Smith & Co. catalogue for $1.00)
$30-$60

King Comics, Flash Gordon

King Comics Set on card (36 rings),
1953 $500 set (each ring occurs in diff. colors)
(Note: most cards have multiple rings of same characters)

ng Comics, Fritz

King Comics, Jiggs?

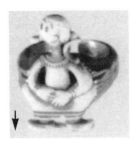

King Comics, Olive Oyl

King Comics, Hans

King Comics, Little Lulu

King Comics, Snuffy Smith

ing Comics, Henry

King Comics, Maggie

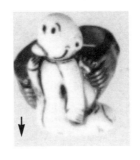

King Comics, Swee'pea

ng Comics, Inspector

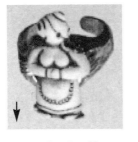

King Comics, Mama

King Features Comics
1953 (set of 20 known)(ceramic material in color)(each ring occurs in diff. colors; Phantom ring has never been seen)
$10-$15 ea.

King Features
1980s (metal cloisonne)
$20-$40

King Vitamin Disc
1970s
$5-$10

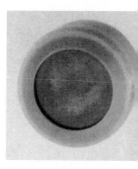

King Vitamin Hologram
1970 (1st hologram ring)
$12-$25

King Features
1950s (Phantom)(thick top)
(in color)
$20-$40

King Features
1950s (Sweeney)(thick top)
(in color)
$20-$40

Kissing Flicker
1970s (gold metal base)
(Hong Kong)
$2-$5

King Features
1950s (Tillie the Toiler)
(thick top, in color)
$20-$40

King Kong
1962 (gumball)(plastic)(base
comes in pink, red, yellow,
green)
$5-$10
in package - $20

Kit Carson T.V.
1950s (scarce)
$200-$300

KKK (see USA/KKK)

Knights of Columbus
View of base used from Green Hornet ring. "G H" (Green Hornet) initials on side of base changed to mean "Holly Ghost."
Good - $750
Fine - $1500
Near Mint - $3000

ights of Columbus
adio), 1940s (rare)(less than 10 known)

Top pivots to reveal glow-in-dark secret compartment with a wax seal over bottom conceiling secret message

Kolonel Keds
1950s (see U.S. Keds)
$30-$60

Krazy Kat
1970s (metal cloisonne)
$50-$100

Lassie Friendship
1950s (metal)(20 carat gold plated)
$90-$180

Knot Hole Gang
1940s (metal)
$20-$60

Here's your
LASSIE FRIENDSHIP RING
and wallet size
PICTURE
of LASSIE and TIMMY
SEE INSIDE...

Kool Aid Treasure
1930s (metal)
$55-$110

Lassie Friendship Ring Paper
1950s (see price on next page)

Lassie Friendship Ring Paper
(Rare), 1950s
$125-$175

Laugh-in Flicker (1)
(16 diff.) "Laugh-in" to Dan & Dick
$10-$20 ea.

Laugh-in Flicker (3)
(16 diff.) Goldie Hawn figure in bikini dancing side to side.
$10-$20 ea.

Laugh-in Flicker (5)
(16 diff.) Henry Gibson as Indian to Henry Gibson as a priest
$10-$20 ea.

Laugh-in Flicker (2)
(16 diff.) Goldie Hawn to Goldie dancing in bikini
$10-$20 ea.

Laugh-in Flicker (4)
(16 diff.) Ruth Buzzi w/hairnet to Ruth Buzzi w/bonnet
$10-$20 ea.

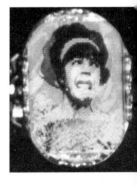

Laugh-in Flicker (6)
(16 diff.) JoAnn Worley sad face to JoAnn Worley screaming
$10-$20 ea.

Laugh-In Vending Machine Display Ring Card
1968 (cardboard, holds 6 Laugh-In rings)(rare)
$50

Laugh-in Flicker (7)
(16 diff.) Beauty (Ruth Buzzi
w/bonnet) to Beast (Dan
Rowan profile)
$10-$20 ea.

Laugh-in Flicker (10)
(16 diff.) "Here Comes the
Judge" to cartoon judge jumping out of circle
$10-$20 ea.

Laugh-in Flicker (13)
(16 diff.) If Minne Hana married
Don Ho" to "She'd be Minne Ha Ha
Ho"
$10-$20 ea.

Laugh-in Flicker (8)
(16 diff.) Artie Johnson as German
soldier "Very Interesting" to "But
Stupid"
$10-$20 ea.

Laugh-in Flicker (11)
(16 diff.) "The Hymns for today
are 76, 81, 92, 85, 42..."to Dick
Martin cartoon yelling "Bingo"
$10-$20 ea.

Laugh-in Flicker (14)
(16 diff.) Circle psychedelic design
to square psychedelic design.
$10-$20 ea.

Laugh-in Flicker(9)
(16 diff.) "Here Comes the
Judge" to Black Man
$10-$20 ea.

Laugh-in Flicker (12)
(16 diff.) "Fickle Finger of Fate
Award" to picture of finger of
Fates Award
$10-$20 ea.

Laugh-in Flicker (15)
(16 diff.) "Goodnight Dick" to
"Who's Dick"
$10-$20 ea.

augh-in flicker (16)
968 (16 diff.)(original silver
se)(vending machine ring)
$10-$20 ea.

Laugh-in Flicker (11)

↑ **Laugh-in T.V. Metal**
1960s (very interesting)
$20-$40 ea.

augh-in Flicker (1)

↑ **Laugh-in Flicker (13)**
(16 diff.), 1968 (blue base)
$10-$20 ea.

Laurel & Hardy
1980s (metal cloisonne)
$50-$100

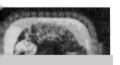

Laugh-in Flicker (4)

Laugh-in T.V. Metal
1960s (here comes the judge)
$20-$40 ea.

**Legion Of Super
Heroes Flight**
1994 (gold, 16 made)(each ring
engraved with a diff. Legion character)
$200 ea.

Lillums (see Post Tin)

Laugh-in Flicker (6)

Laugh-in T.V. Metal
1960s (luv)
$20-$40 ea.

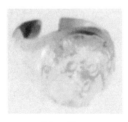

Lion Face
1960s (plastic)
$2-$5

Lionel Printing (Lionel)
1950s (box) (w/stamp pad)(15 pieces)
$175-$225 set

Lil Abner Flicker (1)

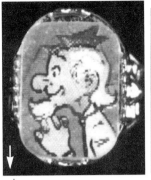

↑ **Lil Abner Flicker (4)**
1960s (silver base)(set of 4)
$8-$15 ea.

Lil Abner Flicker (3)

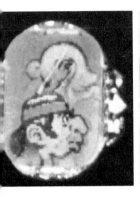

Lil Abner Flicker (2)

↓ **Lil Abner Flicker (1)**

↑ **Lil Abner Flicker (4)**
1960s (blue base)(set of 4)
$5-$10 ea.

Lil Abner Flicker (3)

Lil Abner Flicker (2)

Lips Kiss Flicker
Cloverleaf Milk picture of red lips to
same lips puckering for a kiss.
(also exists in oval form)
1970s
$5-$10

Little King (see Post Tin)

Lone Ranger (see Tonto)

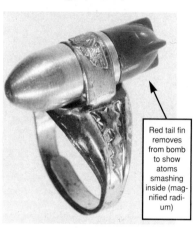

Red tail fin removes from bomb to show atoms smashing inside (magnified radium)

Lone Ranger Atomic Bomb
1946 (Kix cereal) (one of the most popular rings ever given away)(also see Whistle Bomb)
$50-$100

NOTICE

You May Have to Wait
A Few Minutes Before
You Can See the Atomic
Display Inside Ring

Do Not Remove Tail-in Bright Light

Keep red tail-fin on ring you are in the dark. Other you will be unable to see a ic display for approxima half an hour. Removing ta in bright light results in a ste glow inside the atom cham instead of frenzied flashe

HERE'S HOW RING WORKS

1. Take ring into dark room or closet. Close door so that no light can enter.

2. Wait until pupils of eyes dilate—this may take from 2 to 10 minutes. Best and quickest results are obtained at night.

3. Twist red tail-fin on ring until it slides off "bomb".

4. Hold ring close to your eyes. Look into Observation Lens which seals the atom chamber.

5. Keep your eye glued to Observa-

tion Lens. As soon as your eye bec accustomed to the dark you'll se thrilling spectacle of atomic en in action.

HERE'S WHAT YOU'LL SEE—You brilliant flashes of light in the darkness inside the atom cham These frenzied, vivid flashes are cc by the released energy of split a

PERFECTLY SAFE—We guarantee can wear KIX Atomic "Bomb" with complete safety. The atomic terials inside the ring are harmle

Lone Ranger Atomic Bomb Paper
1946 (Kix cereal)
$50-$60

Interchangeable bullets slide on/off shank

Lone Ranger Bullet Ring
(w/two bullets that interchange,a Tonto and a Lone Ranger bullet) (solid silver, 30 made)(38 caliber)
1992
$250 set

Lone Ranger Bullet Ring
(same as 38 caliber, but 22 caliber)
(30 made, solid silver
$250 set

All rings have gem stone insets on base and gold plated lightning bolts

Lone Ranger Bullet Ring
Same as above but showing Tonto Bullet on shank.(fully licensed Overstreet Publ. promotional ring)
$250 set

All Lone Ranger material is copr. Broadway Video Ent.

Lone Ranger Disc
(plastic), 1966
$30-$60

HOW TO PUT BATTERY IN RING

1. Slide battery into opening at bottom of ring band (see picture).

2. Wire "A" should not quite touch button on end of battery.

3. Press Wire "A" lightly against button on battery to light bulb.

Good Deed Order Blank on Other Side

You'll have double fun if you can get your friends to order a Lone Ranger Flashlight Ring, too. Then you can send flash signals back and forth—organize night patrols—play hide and seek in the dark—and lots more things that are big fun. So give the Good Deed Order Blank on opposite side to your best pal and tell him to send for his Lone Ranger Flashlight Ring quick.

Lone Ranger Flashlight paper
1947
$50-$60 (complete)

HOW TO GET EXTRA BATTERIES

For only 10¢ and one Cheerios Boxtop you can get 2 additional batteries. Use Battery Order Blank on opposite side to order.

482   © T. L. R, INC.   (USE BATTERY ORDER BLANK ON OTHER SIDE)

GIVE THIS *Good Deed Order Blank* TO A FRIEND

MAIL TO: LONE RANGER, BOX 1600, MINNEAPOLIS, MINNESOTA

Here's 25¢ and one Cheerios boxtop. Please send my Official Lone Ranger Flashlight Ring complete with 2 batteries and bulb. (DO NOT SEND STAMPS)
Offer expires June 1, 1949

(Print your name here)

(Print your street address here)

(TOWN)   (ZONE)   (STATE)

USE THIS BLANK TO ORDER
Extra Batteries

MAIL TO: LONE RANGER, BOX 1700, MINNEAPOLIS, MINNESOTA
Here's 10¢ and one Cheerio boxtop. Please send my 2 extra batteries. (DO NOT SEND STAMPS)
Offer expires June 1, 1949

(Print your name here)

(Print your street address here)

(TOWN)   (ZONE)   (STATE)

Lone Ranger Flashlight
(w/battery), 1947 (gold color metal)
$50-$100

Real gold ore sealed under clear plastic top

Lone Ranger Gold Ore
(rare) Kelloggs, 1940s (scarce)
Good - $1175
Fine - $2350
Near Mint - $4700

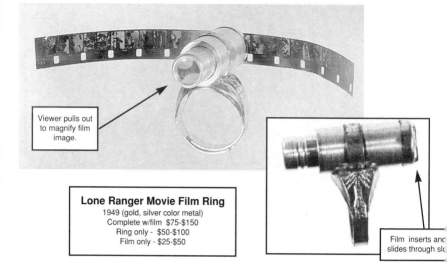

Viewer pulls out to magnify film image.

Lone Ranger Movie Film Ring
1949 (gold, silver color metal)
Complete w/film $75-$150
Ring only - $50-$100
Film only - $25-$50

Film inserts and slides through slot

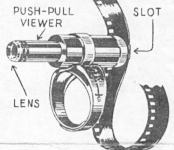

LONE RANGER Movie Film Ring

PUSH-PULL VIEWER

SLOT

LENS

HOW TO OPERATE

1. Slide film into slot on large end of viewer.

2. Hold ring close to your eye and toward light; look into lens.

3. Adjust push-pull viewer until pictures are clear.

Shows *ANY 8 mm. Movie Film*

● For color pictures, black and white, movies taken at home, cartoon film, outdoor shots, indoor pictures—all kind of 8 mm. movie film.

Marine Film Never Before Released

Included with Ring is official U. S. Marine Corps film. Many pictures in film were taken during actual combat and never before released to the public.

SEE OTHER SIDE for *LONE RANGER* "GOOD TURN" ORDER BLANK...

Do a friend a good turn! Give order blank on other side to some boy or girl so that they, too, can get a Lone Ranger Movie Film Ring.

Lone Ranger Movie Film Ring Paper
1949 (see next page for price)

"GOOD TURN" ORDER BLANK

Fill Out and Send at Once

To: LONE RANGER, BOX 1250, Minneapolis, Minnesota

I enclose 20c in coin (no stamps please) plus one Cheerios boxtop. Please rush my Lone Ranger Movie Film Ring plus official U. S. Marine Corps Film. (Good while supplies last.)

_____
(Print your name here)

_____
(Print your address here)

_____
(Town)   (Zone)   (State)

Marine Corps Film — Here's What You See

1. Marine in famous dress blue uniform
2. Marine reconnaissance group going ashore
3. Marines ready to hit the beach
4. Corsair on carrier flight deck
5. Marine reporting to Commander over hand-radio
6. Marine using flame thrower on enemy position
7. Marines advancing on battle field
8. Loading a powerful pack Howitzer
9. Loading explosive rockets into rocket launcher
10. Rockets being fired from Marine rocket launcher
11. Flame Thrower Tank in action
12. Signaling by flag code
13. Marine gun crew loading a heavy caliber field gun
14. Field gun recoiling as it is fired
15. Marine throwing smoke grenade
16. Smoking out enemy with flame thrower
17. Marine flame throwing tank in action
18. Loading rockets into mobile rocket launcher
19. Firing a large Howitzer
20. Ground crew preparing Corsair for take-off
21. Marine searching captured enemy for weapons and important papers
22. A Marine with his war dog
23. Marines raising the American flag after winning the battle
24. Women Marines sending up an electronic weather balloon
25. Marine Corps Honor Guard for the United Nations

A 4617

Lone Ranger Movie Film Ring Paper
1949
$50-$75 (complete)

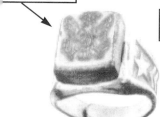

ontains diagonal mirror for seeing at a 45 degree angle

photo of Silver

top fits over base

Lone Ranger National Defenders Look Around
1940s (same as Radio Orphan Annie & Capt. Midnight Mystic Eye)(metal, gold color)
$75-$150

Lone Ranger Photo (Test)
1940s (rare)(gold color metal)
(less than 10 known)
Good - $450, Fine - $900, Near Mint -$1800

Ad from back cover of 1938 Lone Ranger Ice Cream comic book

IMPORTANT!

This Envelope contains

100

Lone Ranger Ice Cream Cone Coupons

TO BE DISTRIBUTED TO YOUR CUSTOMERS

ONE COUPON WITH EACH
LONE RANGER CONE

Lone Ranger Ice Cream
(plastic), 1938
(Advertised in 1938 Lone
Ranger comic book) (rare)
(less than 10 known)(see Tonto)
Good - $875, Fine - $1750, Near Mint - -$3500

He Scanned the Ground for Signs

IMPORTANT: Be sure to tell us
exactly which premium you want, and
to send the right number of coupons
and the correct amount of cash.

Mail to: **The Lone Ranger**
P.O. Box 6308   BALTIMORE, MD.

"Hi-Yo, Silver! Awa

IMPORTANT: Be su
exactly which premium
to send the right numb
to send the correct amou

Mail to: The L
P.O. Box 6308

Lone Ranger Lones
TRADE MARK   REG. 1938

VALUABLE COUPON

This coupon and 10c entitles you to big 52-page **Lone
Ranger** Comic Book, or may be applied against any
other of the **Lone Ranger** premiums described therein.

Enclosed find (   ) I want_____
(LIST ITEM WANTED)

NAME_____
ADDRESS_____
CITY_____   STATE_____

Lone Ranger
Ice Cream paper
1938 (Coupon(s) required when ordering premiums
(ring)(also see Tonto Ice Cream ring)
$250(100 coupons complete with envelope)
(Beware of repo's)

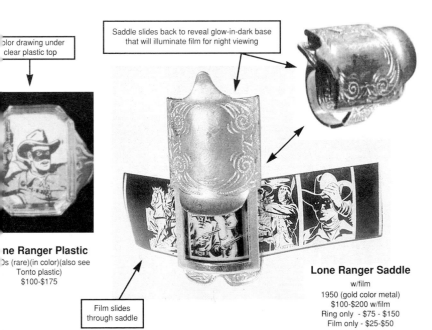

Saddle slides back to reveal glow-in-dark base that will illuminate film for night viewing

...olor drawing under clear plastic top

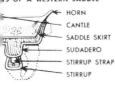

...ne Ranger Plastic
...0s (rare)(in color)(also see Tonto plastic)
$100-$175

Lone Ranger Saddle
w/film
1950 (gold color metal)
$100-$200 w/film
Ring only - $75 - $150
Film only - $25-$50

Film slides through saddle

...TS OF A WESTERN SADDLE

- HORN
- CANTLE
- SADDLE SKIRT
- SUDADERO
- STIRRUP STRAP
- STIRRUP

...iew Film Strip Pictures in the Dark ...

...emove saddle by sliding backwards. The pale green area under ...e is specially prepared to glow in the dark after exposure to ... This material is harmless.

...old the ring near a lightbulb (don't come too close as most ...ulbs become hot) or point it towards the sun. This charges the ...ous paper.

...ide film strip into guide from the side of ring.

...ou can now observe the silhouette pictures in a dark room.

...end Blinker Signals in a Dark Room ...

...irectly expose entire area of luminous paper to light, then ...letely darken room.

...epeatedly cover and uncover the charged luminous paper in ...ness.

...OTE: For bright signals, re-charge luminous paper in film-guide after about four minutes.

...arry Concealed Messages ...

...rite your secret message on a small piece of tissue paper. ...old compactly so that it rests well within the emptied frame of ...lm-guide.

...ide saddle seat back over the film-guide which now serves as a ...rly concealed compartment.

★ INSTRUCTIONS ★
HOW TO HAVE FUN WITH YOUR SADDLE RING

REMEMBER {

LIGHTS ON ... to charge paper or erase pictures and signs.

LIGHTS OUT ... to view pictures and make code signs glow.

FASCINATING EXPERIMENTS!

A. After sliding back saddle, insert film evenly into film-guide over luminous paper. Then hold loaded ring up to light, being careful not to move film. Next remove film from its position over luminous paper. Pictures will mysteriously glow in the darkness.

NOTE: Picture can be instantly erased by direct exposure to light.

B. See how many code signs of your own you can work out. Cut out a triangle, bull's-eye or some such sign from heavy black paper, clipped to fit the film-guide. Expose, then snap out lights, and see your own secret code sign glow through! For dark signs against glowing background heavily mark a piece of tissue paper, and use in same manner as film.

C. After exposing luminous paper in usual manner, allow it to glow in darkness through scene from film strip which you slide back and forth over glowing paper. Note quivering "television effect."

Tell your friends to get a Saddle Ring!   *Order another for yourself!*

Lone Ranger Saddle film paper
printed on thin unstable paper (scarce)
1950, $100-$125

1995   **177**   OVERSTREET PREMIUM RING PRICE GUIDE

**Lone Ranger Seal
Print Face** (metal)
1940s, $150-$300

***Lone Ranger Secret
Compartment-Air Force**
1942 (metal)(scarce)
with Lone Ranger & Silver photos
$375-$750

***Long Ranger Secret
Compartment-Army**
1940s (metal)(scarce)
with photos
$375-$750

***Lone Ranger Secret
Compartment-Marines**
1940s (metal)(scarce)
with photos
$375-$750

***Lone Ranger Secret
Compartment-Navy,**
1940s (metal)(scarce)
with photos
$375-$750

contains flint that emits
sparks when spinned

Lone Ranger Six Shooter
1947 (metal)(silver color handles)
$60-$125

CONTENTS—MERCHANDISE
POSTMASTER: This parcel may
be opened for postal inspection if
necessary.

General Mills, Inc.
400 4th St. So.
MINNEAPOLIS, MINN.

RETURN POSTAGE GUARANTEED

Section 562, P. L. & R.
U. S. POSTAGE
PAID
NEW YORK, N. Y.
Permit No. 5862

**Lone Ranger
Weather** enve-
lope/paper
1947
$50-$75

Clear plastic
top

Ronald Ianetti
70? E 183th St.
Bronx 57 N?

Here's Your
Weather Ring!

Clear plastic
top

Lone Ranger Weather
1947 (metal)
$60-$125
(paper changes color)(also see
Peter Paul Weather)

WARNING!

ALWAYS TAKE THIS RING OFF YO
FINGER BEFORE WASHING YOUR HAN
The reason for this is because the special in
cator material in the ring is very sensit
But . . . if you do get it wet, replace the indica
material in the ring with some of the extra
terial which we enclose in this package.

To replace the indicator material in y
Weather Ring, simply use the point of a pin
pull out the old indicator . . . being careful
to raise the plastic setting. Then trim a piece
the extra indicator material to proper size
carefully slide it into position.

REMEMBER . . .

Don't expect this ring to change with the weath
while you are inside the house! For most sa
factory results, always notice the color of
ring after you have been outside for thirty m
utes. When your ring turns from blue to p
that is an indication that it may rain or sno
When it turns from pink to blue that is an in
cation that it may clear.

*Lone Ranger Secret Compartment rings—Includes photos of silver &
Lone Ranger. Beware of repro photos.

Lone Wolf
(see Thunderbird)

Lone Wolf Tribal
1932 Wrigley (sterling silver)(radio)
(the very first premium ring)
$100-$200

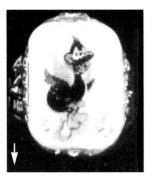

Looney Tunes Flicker
Daffy Duck
jumping and flapping his wings

Looney Tunes Flicker
Henry the Chicken Hawk
kicking an egg

Looney Tunes Flicker
Boxing Kangaroo

Looney Tunes Flicker
Elmer Fudd
firing his rifle

Looney Tunes Flicker
PePe LePew
pinching his nose

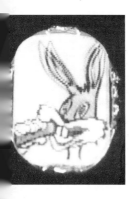

ooney Tunes Flicker
Bugs Bunny
eating a carrot

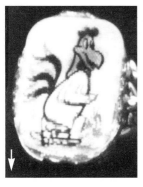

Looney Tunes Flicker
Foghorn Leghorn
walking

Looney Tunes Flicker
Porky Pig
tipping his hat

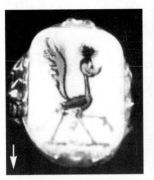

Looney Tunes Flicker
Road Runner
running

Looney Tunes Flicker
Speedy Gonzales
Arms outstretched, then points to himself, then he's gone. Only his hat remains.

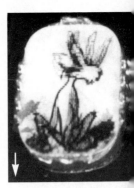

Looney Tunes Flicker
Wile E. Coyote
howling

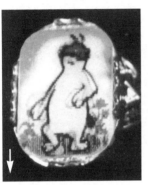

Looney Tunes Flicker
Sam the Sheepdog
dancing around

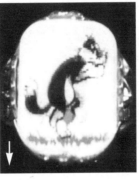

Looney Tunes Flicker
Sylvester
tip-toeing

Looney Tunes Flicker
Yosemite Sam
shooting his guns

Looney Tunes Flicker
1970s (set of 16)(plastic)
(Original flickers on original base)
$8-$15 ea.

Looney Tunes Flicker
Sneezy Mouse
Turning his head raising his hand to his ear

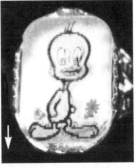

Looney Tunes Flicker
Tweety Bird
looking side to side

Looney Tunes Flicker
Elmer Fudd (modern)

ney Tunes Flicker
Foghorn (modern)

oney Tunes Flicker
Henry Hawk (modern)

ney Tunes Flicker
Porky Pig (modern)

ney Tunes Flicker
90s (modern "v " base)
$2-$5 ea.

L.A. Dodgers
90 (heavy brass & enamel)
Kelloggs Shredded Wheat
cereal premium)
$10-$20

**L.A. Dodgers
World Champions**
(brass & enamel), 1988
$15-$30

Lucky Buddha
1940s
$25-$50

**Lucky Charms
Horseshoe**
(boys), 1985
$60-$120

**Lucky Charms
Horseshoe**
(girls), 1985
$75-$150

Lucky Circus (circus)
1940s(scarce)(large)
$50-$100

Lucky Skull
(see Montrose)

Lucy
1980s (from Snoopy)
(metal cloisonne), $20-$35

Mac (see Post Tin)

Mack
1940s (bronze metal)
$40-$75

Macy's Santa Flicker
1960s (plastic)(Santa Claus to
"Macy's Santa Knows"
$15-$25

Maggie (see Post Tin)

Magic Pup (see Pet Parade)

Magnum P.I.
1981 (plastic)(came on card with
pistols) card with ring - $35
ring only - $15-$25

Majestic Radio
1940s
$75-$150

Man From U.N.C.L.E. Flicker
1960s "U.N.C.L.E." logo to waist up picture of solo blowing smoke off gun (black & white), $50-$75

Man From U.N.C.L. Flicker
1960s "U.N.C.L.E." samlle logo with picture of three m to full figure being shot thro glass(black & white)
$50-$75

Sun exposes film to specially treated paper

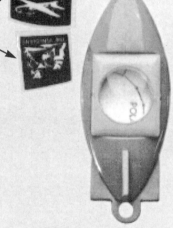

Man From U.N.C.L.E. Flicker
1960s (Face of Solo to face of Ilya), $5-$10

Major Mars Rocket (w/film (4))
1952 (sun exposes film to paper)(also see Captain Video Pendant)
$500-$1000

Mandrake Face
1950s
$20-$40

Marilyn Monro
1950s
$10-$20

Marine Corp.
(plastic), 1950s
$10-$20

Mario
1980s (based on game super
Mario Brothers)
$10-$20

Martian Finks
on card (4 rings), 1950s
$100 card set

Martin Luther King Flicker (1b)
"Martin Luther King" 1918-1968 to Face (front view)

Martin Luther King Flicker (2a)

Martian Finks
(plastic), 1950s (diff. colors)
$10-$20 each

Martin Luther King Flicker (1a)

Martin Luther King Flicker (2b)
"I Have Climbed The Mountain" to Face (profile)

Martin Luther King Flicker (3a)

"Free at Last" to Face (front view)

Martin Luther King Flicker (6a)

"I Have A Dream" to Face (front view)

Martin Luther King Flicker

1964 (set of 6)(plastic)(silver base) $15-$25 ea.

Marvel Flicker (2) Captain America

"Captain America" face to "WUM" Captain America punching enemy

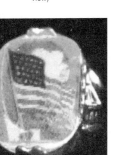

Martin Luther King Flicker (4a)

ture of American Flag to Face (front view)

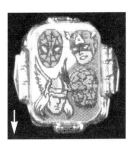

Marvel Flicker (1a) Marvel Super Heroes

Marvel Flicker (3) Dr. Strange Flicker

"Dr. Strange face to full figure Dr. Strange w/arms outstretched

Martin Luther King Flicker (5a)

964 Nobel Peace Prize" to Face (profile)

Marvel Flicker (1b) Marverl Super Heros

"Marvel Super Heroes kRing Club" to 4 faces-Spiderman, Capt. America, Thor, Thing

Marvel Flicker (4a) Fantastic Four

Marvel Flicker (4b)
Fantastic Four
"Fantastic" faces to l"Four" 2 faces

Marvel Flicker (6b)
Human Torch "Human Torch"
face to "Dr. Doom" face

Marvel Flicker (8a)
Spider-Man

Marvel Flicker (5)
Hulk
"Hulk" face to "PAM" Hulk fist
slamming a wall

Marvel Flicker (7a)
Iron Man

Marvel Flicker (8b)
Spider-Man
"Spider-Man" face to full figu
running

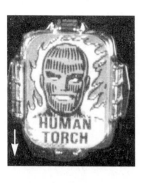

Marvel Flicker (6a)
Human Torch

blron Man Flicker (7b)
"Iron Man" face to "Conk" Iron Man
punching enemy

Marvel Flicker (9)
Spider-Man "Spider-Man" full fi
on a web to "Pow" throwing a pu

**Marvel Flicker (10)
Sub-Mariner**
-Mariner" full figure to "Kop" full fig-
ure left handed punch

**Marvel Flicker (12)
Thor**
"Thor" face to full figure Thor
swinging hammer

**Marvel Flicker (6)
Human Torch**

Marvel Flicker
(plastic silver base), 1970s
(Marvel Entertainment Group)
$10-$20 ea.

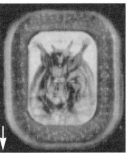

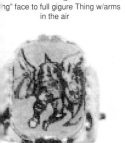

**Marvel Flicker (11)
Thing**
ng" face to full gigure Thing w/arms
in the air

**Marvel Flicker (3)
Dr. Strange**

**Marvel Flicker (7)
Iron Man**

**Marvel Flicker (12)
Thor**

**Marvel Flicker (4)
Fantastic Four**

**Marvel Flicker (8)
Spiderman**

**Marvel Flicker (9)
Spider-Man**

**Marvel Flicker (12)
Thor**

Marvel Flicker
1970s (set of 12)(blue base)
(two diff. blue base versions
shown)(Marvel Ent. Group)
$10-$15 ea.

Marvel Super-Hero Rings
(3 card sets with 2 rings per card), 1980s
$75 complete

**Marvel Flicker (10)
Sub-Mariner**

Marvel Super-Hero Rings
(on card) (3 card sets with 2 rings per card)
1980s
$75 complete

Set includes: Captain
Marvel, Dr. Strange,
Ghost Rider, Hulk,
Spider-Man, Spider
Woman

**Marvel Flicker (11)
Thing**

Marvel Oval
1990s (set of 6)(gumball)(metal)
$1. each

Marvel Super-Hero Rings
(on Card) (3 card sets with 2 rings per card), 1980s
$75 complete

Mask Flicker (1)
(yellow plastic base, blue flicker)

Mask Flicker (2)
(yellow plastic base, blue flicker)

Mask Flicker (3)
(red plastic base, blue flicker)

Mask Flicker (4)
(yellow plastic base, blue flicker)

Mask Flicker (5)

↑

Mask Flicker
1985 (set of 5)(plastic)
movie ring giveaway with card
$20 ea.

Mask Movie Ring
1994 (w/card), $20

McDonald's Big Mac
(plastic), 1970s
$5-$10

McDonald's Grimace

McDonald's McBird

**McDonald's
Ronald McDonald**

**McDonald's
Ham Burgler**

McDonald's McHo

**McDonald's
Character**
(plastic), 1970
$5-$10 ea.

Donald's Figural
1970s (plastic)
$20-$30

McDonald's 500 Smile Race Car
1985 (top & bottom shown)(plastic)
$7-$15

McDonald's Glow Disc
1970s (plastic)
$5-$10

**McDonald's Friendship
Space Shuttle**
1985 (plastic)
$7-$15

McDonald's Flicker (1)
Ronald waving to Ronald on
flying hamburger

McDonald's Flicker (2)
Ronald on diving board to
Ronald splashing as he dives
into pool

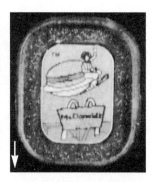

McDonald Flicke's (1)

McDonald's Flicker (4

↑ **McDonald's Flicker**
(set of 4), 1970s (blue base)
$8-$15 ea.

McDonald's Flicker (3)
Ronald standing with jump rope
to Ronald jumping rope

McDonald's Flicker (2)

**McDonald's Halloween
Flicker** (side 1)

McDonald's Flicker (4)
Ronald juggling boalls to same face
moving side to side

↑ **McDonald's Flicker**
1970s (original silver base)
$12-$25 ea.

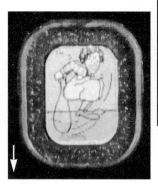

McDonald's Flicker (3)

**McDonald's Halloween
Flicker** (side 2)

↑ **McDonald's Halloween
Flicker**
1970s (plastic) "McDonald's
Halloween to McBoo
$8-$15 ea.

Melvin Purvis Junior G-Man Corps
(Post), 1937 (metal)
$25-$50

Mickey Mouse Club
1950s (red/white/black enamel) (metal)
$30-$60

McDonald's Horn
1980s (plastic)
$40-$75

Mickey Mouse Club
(plastic), 1960s
$35-$70

Melvin Purvis Secret Scarab
Post, 1937
(same as Capt. Hawks Secret Scarab) (rare)
Good $300
Fine $600
Near Mint $1500

McDonald's Valentine
1970s (plastic)(red & white)
$10-$20

Mickey Mouse Club Flicker, 1950s
$25-$50

Melvin Purvis Secret Operator
(Post), 1936 (metal)
$75-$150

Melvin Purvis Birthstone
1930s (metal)
$75-$150

Mets (see Baseball)

Mickey Mouse Club
(Nestles) 1980 (metal)
$40-$80

Mickey Mouse Face
1960s (color)
$5-$10

Mickey Mouse Face
(pewter), 1970s
$75 in box

Mickey Mouse Figure
(brass) 1930s (metal cloisonne)
(1st Mickey ring)
$75-$150

Mickey Mouse Face
(gold plated), 1980s (in box)
$60

**Mickey Mouse Face
Ornament**
1990s, $5-$10

**Mickey Mouse Figure
Cowboy** 1970s
(metal cloisonne)
$30-$60

Mickey Mouse Face
(silver), 1980s
$40

**Mickey Mouse 15th
Anniversary**
1980s
$150 in box

Mickey Mouse Figure
(etched) 1940s (metal)
$50-$100

Mickey Mouse Face
(plastic), 1970s
$2-$5

**Mickey Mouse
Figure, Baby**
1970s (metal cloisonne)
$10-$20

**Mickey Mouse
Figure**
(color), 1980s
$5-$10

Mickey Mouse Figure
Mounted, 1950s
$10-$20

**Mickey Mouse
Small Black Figure**
1980s
(silver & gold versions)
$5-$10

**Mickey Mouse 3D
Figure** (small) 1970s (metal
in color)
$25-$50

Mickey Mouse 3D Figure
(pewter) 1960s (metal)
$30-$60

Mickey Mouse 3D Figure
(large) 1970s
(metal in color)
$25-$50

Mickey Mouse Figure
1990s w/stone (2 examples)
$5-$10

Mickey Mouse Figure
(Santa) 1970s
(metal cloisonne)
$20-$40

Mickey Mouse Figure
1980s (gold color)
$10-$20

Mickey Mouse Locket
1980s (metal, in coloir)(3)
$20-$35 ea.

**Mickey Mouse
Glass Dome**
1930s (brass)(gold color)
(red, black, yellow)
$250-$500

Mickey Mouse Club Flicker
1960s, "Mickey Mouse Club" to Mickey's
face with "member" underneath.
$20-$40

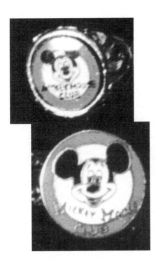

**Mickey Mouse Pearl
Insert**
1990s
$40-$75

Mickey Mouse
(square top (glow-in-dark)
1950s
$50-$100

Mickey Mouse
1980s (round)
$10-$25

Mickey Watch Ring
1970s
$100 in box

**Mickey Mouse Wedding
Band**
1960s (metal cloisonne)
$40-$80

**Mickey Mouse Wrap
Figure**
1970s (metal)
$40-$80

Mickey & Minnie Heart
1992 (metal cloisonne)
$5-$10

Mickey Mouse Novelties
1970s (includes 8 rings)
complete set $75

Mighty Hercules Magic Ring
1960s (on card) (T.V.)(scarce)
complete - $300
Ring only - $100-$175

Mighty Morphin Power Rangers
1993 (5 rings on card)(plastic)
$3.00 complete

Milton Berle Photo
(see Real Photos)

Minnie Mouse Cameo
1980s (metal, in color)
$20-$40

Minnie Mouse Figure
(oval) 1980s (metal)
$10-$20

Minnie Mouse Figure
1970s (metal cloisonne)
$20-$40

**Minnie Mouse
Face**
(plastic)
1970s, $2-$5

**Minnie Mouse
Face**
(oval), 1950s
$10-$20

Minnie Mouse Locket
1980s (metal in color)
$10-$20

Minnie Mouse Figure
1990s (metal)
$5-$10

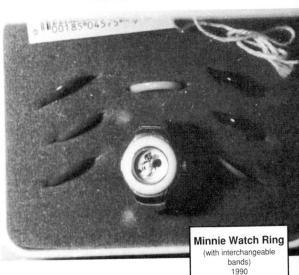

**Minnie Mouse Red
Face**
1980s (metal cloisonne)
$10-$20

Minnie Watch Ring
(with interchangeable
bands)
1990
$100 set

**Minnie Mouse
Stamp**
(came in box as shown)
1992 (5 diff.)
$10 ea.

Mr. Magoo set
(3 rings, Mr. Magoo, Charlie & Waldo)
1960s
$30 - set in bag
ring only - $4-$8 ea.

Miss Packman
1980s (metal)
$15-$30

Charlie

Mr. Magoo

Waldo

Mr. Magoo
1960s
$4-$8 ea.

Mr. Peanut
0s (silver color metal)
$25-$50

ter Softee Face,
1950s (plastic)
$25-$50

ster Softee Flicker
s "I Like Mister Softee" to
e of Mr. Softee (silver base)
$50-$100

odel Airplane club
1940s
$50-$100

Monkey Flicker
1950s (Thick top)
$10-$20

Monkees Flicker (2)
"Mickey" Face
to full figure playing drums

Monkees Flicker (1a)
(side 1) "Davy" face

Monkees Flicker (3a)
(side 1) "Mike face to full figure
playing guitar

Monkees Flicker (1b)
(side 2) "Davy" Face to full Figure
playing guitar

Monkees Flicker (3b)
(side 2) "Mike" Face
to full figure playing guitar

Monkees Flicker (4)
"Peter" Face
to full figure playing base

Monkees Flicker (6)
"I Love Monkees" Logo
w/hearts to four figures in
water on surfboard

Monkees Flicker (9)
Davy & Mickey playing guitar &
drums on unicycles to Peter playing base on pogo stick & Mike
playing guitar on skate board

Monkees Flicker (5a)
(4 Heads), 1966
$20-$40

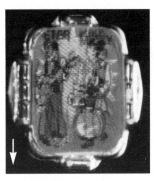

Monkees Flicker (7)
"Peter" & "Mickey" full figures
playing bass & drums to "Davy" &
"Mike" full figures playing guitars

Monkees Flicker (10)
"Monkees" logo to 4 figures in
Monkee Mobile

(no photo available)

Monkees Flicker (5b)
"I Love Monkees" Logo
to four heads w/heart in middle

Monkees Flicker (8)
"I love Peter Micky" two faces
smiling to The Monkees Day Mike
two faces

Monkees Flicker (11)
Old fashioned camera w/two guys
holding flash to two figures one
standing, one sitting

Monkees Flicker (12)
"Official member Monkees ring club"
to four faces in a red heart

Monkees Flicker
1966 (12 different)
All rings distributed in cereal
boxes sealed in paper
$30-$60 ea.

Monster Fink Rings on Card
1960s (plastic)
Complete -$100
Ring only - $8-$15 ea.

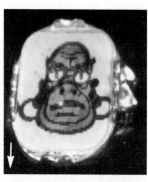

Monster Cartoon Flicker
Fat green one-tooth goon with earrings
to skinny white guy with forehead scar.

Monster Cartoon Flicker
White face phantom to red face
Frankenstein looking character.

Monster Cartoon Flicker
Green face Frankenstein to red face
devil with pointed teeth and big ears.

↑ **Monster (cartoon)
Flicker**
(set of 3), 1960s (plastic)
$20-$40 ea.

Montrose Lucky Skull
(see Skull)

**Movie Star Photo
Allyson, June**
1940s, $15-$25

**Movie Star Photo
Cooper, Gary**
1940s, $15-$25

**Movie Star Photo
Gibb, Andy**
1980s, $5-$10

**Movie Star Photo
Granger, Farley**
1940s, $15-$25

**Movie Star Photo
Kelly, Gene**
1940s, $15-$25

**Movie Star Photo
Mature, Victor**
1940s, $15-$25

**Movie Star Photo
Taylor, Elizabeth**
1940s, $25-$50

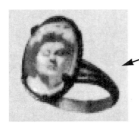

**Movie Star Photo
Winters, Shelly**
1940s, $15-$25

Mork & Mindy Flicker (1a)

Mork & Mindy Flicker (2)
"Mork NA-NO, NA-NO to "Hello Mindy"
1979, $20-$35

Mork & Mindy Flicker (1b)
"Shazbot;" to "Mork Calling Orson"
1979, $20-$35

Mork & Mindy Flicker (3)
"Mork from Ork" to "Mindy's Friend"
1979, $20-$35

Mummy (see Universal Monsters)

Munster Flicker (Herman)
Picture of Herman to "Herman
Munsters"

**Munster Flicker (Grandpa
Munster)**
Picture of Granpa to "Grandpa
Munsters"

Munsters Flickers
1960s (silver base, set of 4)
$25-$50 ea.

**Munster Flicker
(Herman Munster)**

Munster Flicker (Lily)
Picture of Lily to "Lily Munsters"

**Munster Flicker
(Eddie Munster)**

**Munster Flicker
(Lily Munster)**

Munster Flicker (Eddie)
Picture of Eddie & Wolfie to "Eddie
Munsters"

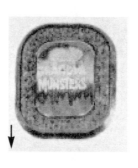

**Munster Flicker
(Grandpa Munster)**

Munsters flickers
1960s (blue base, set of
$20-$40 ea.

**Mutant Ninja
Turtles**
(see Teenage--)

Mutley (see Wacky
Races)

**Mysterymen of
America**
1992 (prototype)(metal)
(Bob Burden)
$15-$25

Nabisco Compass
(see compass--)

National Baseball
(see Baseball, Nationals)

w York World's Fair Flicker
1964-65 (plastic)(2 diff.)
$8-$15 ea.

**NFL Football Logo
Atlanta Falcons**

**NFL Football Logo
Buffalo Bills**

**NFL Football Logo
Chicago Bears**

**NFL Football Logo
Cin. Bengals**

**NFL Football Logo
Cleveland Browns**

**NFL Football Logo
Dallas Cowboys**

**NFL Football Logo
Denver Broncos**

**NFL Football Logo
Detroit Lions**

**NFL Football Logo
Green Bay Packers**

**NFL Football Logo
Houston Oilers**

NFL Football Logo
Indianapolis Colts

NFL Football Logo
New England Patriots

NFL Football Logo
Phoenix Cardinals

NFL Football Logo
Kansas City Chiefs

NFL Football Logo
New Orleans Saints

NFL Footb all Logo
Pittsburg Steelers

NFL Football Logo
L.A. Rams

NFL Football Logo
New York Giants

NFL Football Logo
San Francisco 49'ers

NFL Football Logo
Miami Dolphins

NFL Football Logo
New York Jets

NFL Football Logo
Seattle Seahawks

NFL Football Logo
Minnesota Vikings

NFL Football Logo
Oakland Raiders

NFl Football Logo
Tampa Bay Buccanee

NFL Football Logo
Washington Redskins

↑ **NFL Football Logo**
(28 diff.) (Kelloggs)
$20-$40 ea.

New York Mets
(see baseball)

New York Yankees
(see baseball)

Nightmare
1982 (plastic)(black over white)
$15-$30

Nixon (see President Nixon)

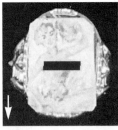

↑ **Nude Flicker**
1960s (plastic)
$5-$10 ea.

Olive Oyl (see Post Tin)

Olympic Ring
1950s, $30-$60

Operator 5 (pulp)
1934 (rare)(metal)(less than 10
examples known)

Good - $3333
Very Good - $5335
Fine - $8335
Very Fine - $14,170
Near Mint - $20,000

Orphan Annie
(see Post Tin & Radio--)

Oscar Meyer Weiner
(plastic) (red & yellow)
$10-$20

Ovaltine Birthday
1930s (same as Radio
Orphan Annie Birthday)
$100-$200

Ovaltine Signet
1937 (metal)
$30-$60

Pac Man
1980 (metal)(yellow)
$15-$25

Pac Man
1980s (cereal)
$15-$25

Pac Man (see Miss Pac Man)

Paladin
(see Have Gun Will Travel)

Pan American Clipper
(cereal), 1950s
$30-$60

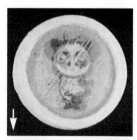

Panda Flicker
1980s (set of 4)
$5-$10 ea.

Paul Winchell & Jerry Mahoney Photo
(see Real Photos)

Pe Pe LePew (see Looney Tur|

Pepsi Cola
1980s (metal, in color)
$5-$10

Perry Winkle
(see Post Tin)

Magic magnetic ring collar makes magic pup do tricks

Pet Parade Pup & Magic Ring
(Wheat Chex) (w/magnet ring collar), 1950s
$60-$120

Here's Your **PET PARADE PUP...** ...and **MAGIC RING**

and here are some of the Tricks He'll Do!

He'll grab one end of ring...turn away from the other

He hops toward you

Turns his head, nods "YES" or shakes his head "NO"

Rolls eyes

Catches pins, paper clips if ring is on nose

Opens mouth. Snaps! Bites!

and you can do AMAZING TRICKS with ring alone

PICK UP SHEETS OF PAPER... by hiding pin or paper clip underneath. Magnetic power goes right through paper.

MAKE THUMB TACKS GO CRAZY. Put tack on top of sheet of paper. Move hand (with ring) in circles against underside of paper. Tack will follow ring.

LEND TO MOM... to pick up dropped pins and needles when she's sewing.

Your friends can order a **PET PARADE PUP** and **MAGIC RING**

Just mail this coupon with **WHEAT CHEX** or **RICE CHEX** box top and **25¢**

Pet Parade and Magic Pup Paper
1950s (large size)
$75-$85

Peter Paul Face
1950s (plastic)
$15-$25

PF Flyer Decoder
1949 (plastic)
$20-$40

**Peter Paul
Glow-in-Dark
Secret Compartment**
1940s (metal)
$175-$350

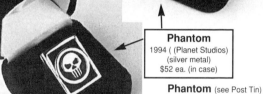

Phantom
1994 ((Planet Studios)
(silver metal)
$52 ea. (in case)

Phantom (see Post Tin)

Phantom (see Universal Monste

Peter Paul Weather
1950s (also see Lone
Ranger Weather)
$25-$50

Phantom Ring on Card
1991 (3 diff.)(metal), $25 ea. complete
on card

Phantom Ring on Card
1991 (3 diff.)(metal)
$25 each complete on card

Phantom Ring on Card
1991 (rings from card)(3 diff.)
(close-up view)(see previous page)
$25 ea. (complete on card)

Phantom
(see King Features

Pinocchio Figure
1970s (metal, cloisonne)
$40-$75

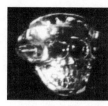

Pirates of Carribean
1980s
$5-$10

Phantom (metal)
1970s (gold color)
$100
(distr. in England)

Pinocchio Tell The Truth
1940s
$200-$400

Pirate Glow Skull
1940s (plastic)
$50-$75

Pittsburg Pirates (see Bowman Gum)

Pharoah
1950s (dark amber
see-through top
$30-$60

Pinocchio
1980s (metal, gold color)
$50-$100

Planet of the Apes
1970s (metal, green)
$25-$50

Pinooacchio Figure
1960s (3D figutre) (metal in color)
$40-$80

Pirate
1980s
$5-$10

Planet of the Apes
1970s (metal, green)
$25-$50

Poll Parrot (see Howdy Doody)

Pluto (colored & plain)
International, silver
1950s
$50-!00

Pluto (paper disc)
1980s
$1-$2

Poll Parrot Face
(gold & silver versions)
1950s
$20-$40

Pluto (Glow-in-dark)
1950s
$50-$100

Pocahontas
1960s
$10-$20

Polly Pocket
(10 diff.), 1990s
(4 diff. series of
6-8 rings in each)
$2-$4 ea.

Polly Pocket Box
1990s
$2-$5

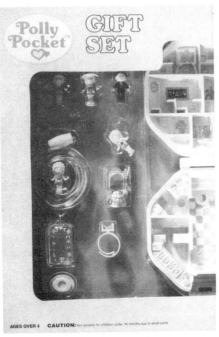

Polly Pocket Gift Set
1990s
$2-$5

Popeye
1980s (Metal cloisonne)
$15-$25

Popeye (see Post Tin & Wimpy)

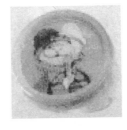

Popeye
1960s
$10-$20

Polly Pocket Throne
1990s
$5-$10

Popeye
1993 (staber)(Silver)
(36 produced)
$185

opeye Flicker (1a)
960s, Popeye to Wimpy
(blue base)
(side 1) $10-$20 ea.

opeye Flicker (1b)
960s, Popeye to Wimpy
(blue Base)(side 2)
$10-$20 ea.

Popeye Flicker
4 diff.) 1960s, (blue base)
$10-$20 ea.

Popeye Flicker (2)
1960s, Popeye to Olive Oyl
(silver base)
$15-$25

Popeye Flicker (3)
1960s, Popeye to Wimpy
(silver base)
$15-$25

**Popeye Vending Machine
Ring Paper**
1960s (in color)
$15-$30

Popsicle Skull (see Skull)

Top swivels open to
reveal secret compart-
ment and paper code

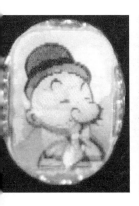

Popeye Flicker (1)
1960s, Popeye to Sweet Pea
(silver base)
$15-$25

Popeye Flicker (4)
1960s, Popeye to bucktooth nephew
(silver base)
$15-$25

Popsicle Boot
(with paper code), 1951
complete $50-$100
no paper $37-$75

Post Tin - Casper, $5-$25

Porky Pig
(hand painted) (metal)
1970
$7-$14

Porky Pig Flicker
(see Arby's, Daffy Duck & Looney Tunes)

Post Tin Rings
(unbent examples
with no rust are rare), 1948,
1949 (cereal premiums)
(in color) (priced below)

Post Tin - Casper, $5-$25

Post Tin - Alexander, $5-$25

Post Tin - Dagwood, $10-$50

Post Tin - Andy Gump, $5-$25

Post Tin - Dale's Brand (Roy Rogers), $8-$4

Post Tin - Bullet (Roy Rogers), $8-$40

Post Tin - Deputy Sheriff (Roy Rogers)
$8-$40

Post Tin - Captain, $5-$25

Post Tin - Dick Tracy $20-$100
No Picture

Post Tin - Felix the Cat, $20-$100

Post Tin - Flash Gordon, $20-$100
No Picture

Post Tin - Fritz, $5-$25

Post Tin - Hans, $5-$25

Post Tin - Harold Teen, $5-$25

Post Tin - Henry, $5-$25

Post Tin - Herby, $5-$25

Post Tin - Inspector, $5-$25

Post Tin - Jiggs, $5-$25

Post Tin - Lillums, $5-$25

Post Tin - Little King, $10-$50

Post Tin - Mac, $5-$25
No Picture

Post Tin - Maggie, $5-$25

Post Tin - Mamma, $5-$25

Post Tin - Olive Oyl, $10-$50

Post Tin - Roy's Boots, $8-$40

Post Tin - Orphan Annie, $10-$50

Post Tin - Roy's Brand, $8-$40

Post Tin - Perry Winkle, $5-$25

Post Tin - Roy's Holster, $8-$40

Post Tin - Phantom, $20-$100

Post Tin - Sheriff (Roy Rogers), $8-$40

Post Tin - Popeye, $20-$100

Post Tin - Skeezix, $5-$25

Post Tin - Roy Rogers, $12-$50

Post Tin - Smilin' Jack, $10-$50

Post Tin - Smitty, $5-$25
(no picture)

Post Tin - Smokey Stover, $5-$25
(no picture)

Post Tin - Snuffy Smith, $10-$50
(no picture)

Post Tin - Swee' pea, $10-$50
(no picture)

Post Tin - Toots, $10-$50

Post Tin - Tillie The Toiler, $5-$25

Post Tin - Trigger (Roy Rogers), $8-$40

Post Tin - Wimpy, $10-$50

Post Tin - Winnie Winkle, $5-$25
(no picture)

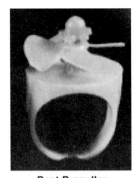

Post Propeller
1960s (plastic), $25-$35

Power Rangers (see Mightty Morphin)

President Nixon Flicker
President Nixon's visit to Peking
21st Feb. 1972 to faces of Nixon
$15-$30

President Nixon Flicker
1970s, Faces of Nixon & Mao
Tse Tung to Faces of Nixon &
Cho En Lai with Great Wall of
China in background.
$15-$30

**Quake Figural,
Captain** (plastic)
1960s
$250-$500
(also see Quisp Figural)

Quaker
1940s (metal)
$75-$150

Quaker Friendship
1950s, $40-$80

Quaker Jingle Bell
1950s
$15-$30

Quaker Meteor
1950s (w/meteorite enclosed)
$15-$30

Quaker Pencil Sharpener
1950s
$15-$30

Quaker Puzzle
1950s
$15-$30

Quaker Puzzle
1950s (tic tac toe)
$15-$30

Quaker Ship-in-Bottle
1950s
(Also see Capt. Crunch)
$15-$30

Quaker Siren
1950s
$15-$30

Quaker Water Pistol
1950s
$15-$30

Quaker Whistle
1950s
$15-$30

↑ **Quaker Crazy Ring**
(above)
(10 diff.), 1950s
(priced individually)

KIDS! GET COMPLETE SET OF 10

CRAZY RINGS

ALL 10 YOURS FOR ONLY 25¢

AMAZING! JUST LOOK AT WHAT THEY DO!

SIREN RING
This one makes a noise just like fire-engine!

PENCIL SHARPENER RING
Actually sharpens pencil while you're wearing it!

PUZZLE RINGS
With a little practice you'll amaze people by solving puzzles while actually wearing your *Crazy Puzzle Rings!*

WAIT'LL YOU SHOW YOUR FRIENDS!

WATER PISTOL RING
Point your finger, push the plunger and it shoots!

SHIP-IN-A-BOTTLE RING
A perfect ship completely enclosed in the tiny bottle!

WHISTLE RING
Blow powerful signal just by lifting your finger!

There's a Crazy Ring for every finger! Send for all 10 now.

FRIENDSHIP RING
Tiny hands clasp and unclasp in friendly handshake!

METEOR RING
Contains an actual meteor piece from outer space!

JINGLE BELL RING
Get attention by raising your hand and ringing the bell!

CRAZY RINGS, BOX 200, NEW YORK 46, N.Y.

SEND THIS ORDER BLANK TODAY TO:

Please send me a complete set of 10 Crazy Rings.
I enclose 25¢ in cash (no stamps, please)

Name _____
(Please print)

Address _____

City _____ Zone ____ State ____

This offer good only in U. S. and while supply lasts.
Void where prohibited, taxed, or regulated.

Quaker Crazy Ring Paper, 1950s, $20-$40

Quaker Volcano Whistle
1960s (complete in package)
$350

Quaker Initial Ring
1939 (metal)
$100-$200

Quick Draw McGraw
w/Huckleberry Hound Ring
1960s
$37-$75

(also see Baba Looey and Zorro for
other glove and ring sets)

**Quisp Friendship
Figural**
1960s (plastic)(assembled)
$900-$1500

**Quisp Friendship
Figural** (also see Quake
Figural)

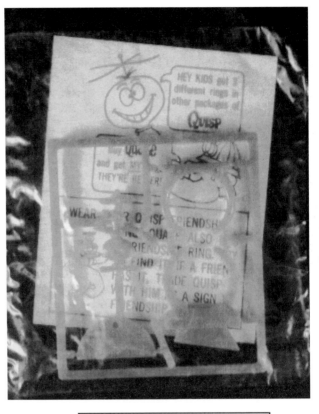

Quisp Friendship Figural
Cereal, (packaged on tree w/papers)
1960s
$1600 complete in bag

**Quisp Space Disk
Whistle**
1960s
$175-$350

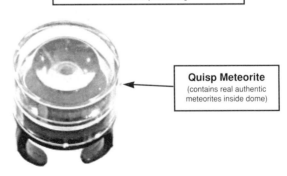

Quisp Meteorite
(contains real authentic
meteorites inside dome)

Quisp Meteorite
1960s (plastic)
$175-$350

Quisp Paper
1960s (back of cereal box)
$40-$75

Radio Orphan Annie
(see Post Tin)

Radio Orphan Annie Birthday
1936
(same as Ovaltine Birthday)
$100-$200

Rabbit Flicker
1950s (thick top)
$15-$30

Rabbit Flicker
1990s ("v" base, silver)
$5-$10

From
RADIO'S LITTLE ORPHAN ANNIE
180 North Michigan Avenue
Chicago, Illinois

See next page

Made to Fit You Automatically
If your ring is a little too small in size when you get it, you can simply pry it open a little at a time until it is the correct size. In case it is too large, it can be squeezed together until it fits your finger exactly.

Imported Stone
The beautiful stone in your ring is a hand-made simulated birthstone. It was made over in Europe and imported to this country. You should always take off a stone set ring when you wash your hands—because soap gets in under the stone—and keeps it from sparkling.

● Your Orphan Annie birthstone ring is made out of a special metal—finished with genuine 24 karat gold-plate, with a special rose-gold finish! After it is plated with gold—each ring is coated with lacquer to help protect the gold! As long as you wear your ring every day it will stay bright. If, for any reason, you lay it aside—it may lose some of its brightness—but you can make it shiny again simply by washing it off with soap and water and rubbing it a few times over any soft rough surface such as a carpet.

HERE'S YOUR **Orphan Annie** BIRTHDAY RING

LOOK INSIDE! See the Birthday Sentiment, Sign and Flower for the Month in Which You Were Born!

HERE ARE THE BIRTHSTONES AND BIRTHDAY SIGNS, FLOWERS AND SENTIMENTS FOR EACH MONTH OF THE YEAR!

You can have lots of fun reading this list—and seeing what flower, sign and sentiment goes with **your** birthday—and the birthdays of your father and mother and all your friends!

MONTH	*BIRTHSTONE	FLOWER	SENTIMENT	SIGN
January	Garnet	Snowdrop	Constancy	Good Health, Victory
February	Amethyst	Carnation	Sincerity	Against Intoxication
March	Aquamarine	Violet	Wisdom	Social Success
April	White Sapphire	Easter Lily	Upright	Happy Marriage
May	Green Spinel	Hawthorn	Esteem	Fame, Immortality
June	Alexandrite	Rose	Wealth	Purity, Innocence
July	Ruby	Daisy	Freedom	Good Fortune
August	Peridot	Water Lily	Friendship	Prudence
September	Sapphire	Poppy	Truth	For Beautiful Thoughts
October	Rose Zircon	Cosmos	Hope	Power of Learning
November	Golden Sapphire	Chrysanthemum	Loyalty	Removes Fear
December	Zircon	Holly	Success	Soul Cheerer

*Modern list of birthstones approved by the Association of Stone Dealers.

HOW TO GET MORE RINGS

If your brother or sister or friend want to get one of these Orphan Annie Birthday rings when they see you wearing yours—tell them here's all they have to do: Print their name and address and BIRTHDAY plainly on a piece of paper—showing the **month** in which they were born. Then send it in, together with all of the thin round aluminum seal from underneath the lid of a can of Ovaltine—and also a 10c piece! Mail it to:—Little Orphan Annie, 180 N. Michigan Avenue, Chicago, Illinois! But tell them they'll have to act fast—because only a limited supply of these simulated birthstones were imported from Europe—so this offer holds good only as long as the supply of rings last!

Radio Orphan Annie Birthday Paper
1930s
(complete) $50-$60

Radio Orphan Annie Face
1930s (metal, gold color)
$50-$100

Fitted prongs

Radio Orphan Annie Face
1980s (metal cloisonne)
$10-$20

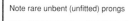

Note rare unbent (unfitted) prongs

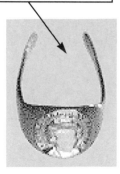

Radio Orphan Annie Face
(rare unbent prongs)
1930s (metal, gold color)
$120

Radio Orphan Annie Face
1980s (metal cloisonne)
$10-20

Radio Orphan Annie & Sandy
1980s (metal cloisonne)
$10-$20

Top contains two openings and a diagonal mirror inside enabling the viewer to look around corners

Radio Orphan Annie Mystic Eye
1930s (same as Lone Ranger Ntl. Defender & Capt. Midnight Mystic Eye Detector)
$95-$190

he altitude of
my planes can
determined by
atching size of
o-through holes
with plane

nall metal
es pivot out
eveal small
ep holes for
wing planes

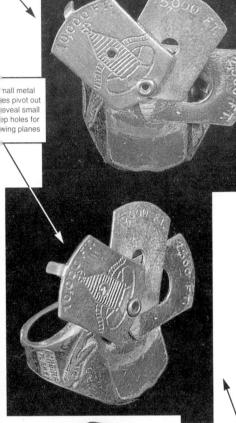

Radio Orphan Annie
Secret Guard Initial
1940s (rare)(gold color metal)(red letter)
Good - $1200
Fine - $2400
Near Mint - $4800

Magnifying glass on top
swings out

Radio Orphan Annie Secret
Guard Magnifying (also see Valric
The Viking), 1940s (rare)(metal)
Good - $1125
Fine - $2250
Near Mint - $4500

Radio Orphan
Annie
Secret Guard
Altascope
1940s (very rare)
(Less than 10 known, one in
near mint)(World War II pre-
mium)
Good - $4,170
Very Good - $7,290
Fine - $10,415
Very Fine - $17,700
Near Mint - $25,000

Radio Orphan Annie Signet
1930s (metal)
$150-$300

Radio Orphan Annie Silver Star, 1930s (metal)
$200-$450

Ring whowing topand inside together

Complete with top intack

Radio Orphan Annie Triple Mystery
showing top and secret compartment
complete $300-$1200

Radio Orphan Ann Triple Mystery
(secret compartment)
1930s (complete)
Good - $300
Fine - $600
Near Mint - $1200

Ring with top missir
$50-$100

Radio Orphan Anni Triple Mystery
with top removed

2-Initial Signet Ring Paper
(see price on next page)

Radio Orphan Annie 2-Initial Signet
1930s (metal)
$110-$220

Here's the Orphan Annie
2-INITIAL
SIGNET RING
WE MADE UP TO YOUR ORDER

INSIDE—See How To Make Your
Seal With This Ring. ALSO—How
To Get Gift To Surprise Your
Mother on Mother's Day!

How Your 2-Initial Signet Ring Makes Personal Seals Like This

ur Orphan Annie Two-Initial g is a true Signet Ring. It will ke your own *personal seal* in wax n a way that no one can coun- it.

course, when you use your ring a seal, it prints your initials *kwards*—so it makes a fine ret seal that your friends will al- rs recognize.

e's how to use your ring to make your personal l:

. Just let some candlewax or sealing wax drip on flap of your envelope.

. Wet the front of your ring with your tongue. is keeps the ring from sticking to the wax.

. Then press the front of your ring firmly down o the wax—while it's still soft.

. Lift the ring—and you see the impression of ir own initials in the wax, sharp and clear—and nted BACKWARDS!

ce you make this seal on a letter, nobody can nper with its contents without it showing. ause they will have to *break* the seal before they n the letter. Even if they melted the wax smooth in, it wouldn't do any good—because they can't ke a seal like yours—without having your Two- tial Signet Ring!

How To Care For Your 2-Initial Signet Ring

Your Orphan Annie Signet Ring was specially made up to your order—with your two initials set in the top.

The ring is made of a special gold-colored metal— finished with genuine 24-karat gold plate. Then, it is coated with lacquer to help protect the gold. The initials and top section are solid nickel silver.

If you wear your ring every day, it will stay bright! However, if you don't happen to wear it for awhile, and it becomes dull—you can make it shiny again by rubbing it a few times over any soft, rough sur- face, such as a carpet.

NOTE:—Your initials are "set" in this ring some- thing like the way jewels are set in rings. You should always take off a "set" ring of this type when you wash your hands, because soap can get under and around the initials and keeps them from shining.

Made to Fit You Automatically

If your ring is a little too small in size when you get it, you can simply pry it open a little at a time until it is the correct size. In case it is too large—it can be squeezed together until it fits your finger exactly.

(See Next Page)

Radio Orphan Annie 2-Initial paper
1930s
$60-$80

Raggedy Ann Face
1980s (metal, cloisonne)
$10-$20

Raggedy Anne Figure
1980s (metal cloisonne)
$5-$10

Randolf Scott Photo
(see Real Photos)

Range Rider (T.V.)
1950s
$100-$200

Range Rider (T.V.)
(rare), 1950s
$250-$500

Raggedy Ann
(metal)(in color)
$5-$10

Ranger Rick (T.V.)
1950s, $50-$100

Rat Fink (complete in bag)
1950s, $20 in bag, ring only - $5-$10

Real Photos
Autry, Gene Photo
1950s, $10-$20

Real Photos
Benny, Jack Photo
1950s, $10-$20

Real Photos
Cassidy, Hopalong
Photo
(William Boyd), 1950s, $12-$25

Real Photos
Crosby, Bing Photo
1950s, $10-$20

Real Photos
Berle, Milton Photo
1950s, $10-$20

Real Photos
Cooper, Gary Photo
1950s, $10-$20

Real Photos
Durante, Jimmy Photo
1950s, $10-$20

Real Photos card with rings
(round) 1940s, 1950 (store), 1960s
$10-$20 ea. (set $250)
(cowboy & T.V. stars)

**Real Photos
Gleason, Jackie Photo**
1950s, $12-$25

**Real Photos
Hayworth, Rita Photo**
1950s, $10-$20

**Real Photos
Louis, Joe Photo**
1940s, $20-$40

**Real Photos
Godfrey, Arthur Photo**
1950s, $10-$20

**Real Photos
Hope, Bob Photo**
1950, $10-$20

**Real Photos
MacArthur, Dougla
Photo**
1950s. $10-$20

**Real Photos
Grable, Betty Photo**
1950, $12-$25

**Real Photos
Kennedy, Jackie Photo**
1960s, $5-$10

**Real Photos
McCarthy, Charlie
Photo**
1950s. $10-$20

**Real Photos
Hayes, Gabby Photo,**
1950s, $10-$20

**Real Photos
Kennedy, John Photo**
1960s, $5-$10

**Real Photos
McCrae, Joel Phot**
1950s, $10-$20

Real Photos
ogers, Roy Photo
1950s, $15-$30

Real Photos
Sinatra, Frank Photo
1950s, $10-$20

Real Photos
Sullivan, Ed Photo
1950s, $10-$20

Real Photos
ogers, Roy Photo
1950s, $15-$30

Real Photos
Starrett, Charles Photo
1950s (round) (store)
$10-$20

Real Photos
Wayne, John Photo
1950s, $20-$40

Real Photos
cott, Randolf Photo
(profile)
1950s, $10-$20

Real Photos
John Wayne Photo
1950 (rectangle)
$50-$100

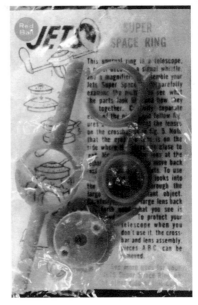

Real Photos
ott, Randolf Photo
1950s, $12-$25

Real Photos
Winchell, Paul &
Jerry Mahoney Photo
1950s, $10-$20

Red Ball Super Space Decoder
(in bag, on tree)
1950s, $15-$30

FREE! AT NO EXTRA COST!

PLASTIC

Top swings out to reveal secret compartment

Red Goose Secret Compartment
1940s
$60-$120

Republic XF-91 Paper
$40-$50

ONE RING IN EVERY BOX OF
Kellogg's PEP

16 Different Pictures!
6 Bright Colors!

No Waiting—
No Box Tops!

WHAT YOU GET! Open a box of Kellogg's PEP and you get your prize! A bright-colored, genuine plastic ring with a picture on top! Pictures of airplanes, cowboys, Indians, sport stars, movie stars! These prize picture rings fit any finger! Get PEP today—the "build up" wheat cereal! Crisp, delicious wheat flakes you're sure to enjoy!

Surprise—entirely new series of prizes coming soon.

Wear 'em! Collect 'em! Swap 'em!

Red Ryder 1940s
(metal), $100-$200

Republic F-84E Thunderjet
(cereal), 1950s, $30-$60

Rin Tin Tin (Cpl. Boone)

Rin Tin Tin Geronimo

Republic XF-91 Thundercepter
(cereal) 1950s
$30-$60

Rin Tin Tin Fort Apache

Rin Tin Tin Horse

**Rin Tin Tin
Lt. Rip Masters**

**Rin Tin Tin
Rinty & Rusty**

**Rin Tin Tin
Rusty**

**Rin Tin Tin
Major**

Rin Tin Tin

**Rin Tin Tin
Sgt. Biff**

↑ **Rin Tin Tin**
1960s (plastic)
(12 diff.)(Nabisco Rice
Honeys cereal premium)
$10-$20 ea.

← **Rin Tin Tin**

HERE IT IS!

YOUR

RIN TIN TIN

MAGIC RING!

Rin Tin Tin paper
(outside) for magic ring
1950s
(see next page for price)

YOUR NEW MAGIC RING —

☆ Fits any finger

☆ Contains hidden ink pad

☆ Includes extra strips of message paper

☆ Has magic pencil that writes invisible
messages on white paper

Use this coupon to get more
MAGIC RINGS. They're great
gifts to give your friends.

RING
P. O. Box 95, New York 46, N. Y.

Please send .... MAGIC RING(S). (25¢ and box top for each).
Each ring complete with magic pencil and message paper.

NAME_____

ADDRESS_____

CITY_____ZONE_____STATE_____
PLEASE PRINT PLAINLY

WRITE INVISIBLE MESSAGES LIKE A SECRET AGENT

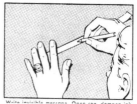

Rin Tin Tin Magic paper (inside)
1950s
(complete) $100-$125

• EASY TO LOAD •

YOU'LL GET LOADS OF FUN WITH
THIS SECRET RING ON YOUR FINGER.
IT SHOOTS PAPER CAPS
THAT MAKE A LOUD BANG LIKE A
REAL GUN... BUT IT IS ABSOLUTELY
SAFE AND HARMLESS.
RING SIZE ADJUSTABLE
HEAD OF RING CAN ALSO BE USED
TO CONCEAL A SMALL PHOTOGRAPH.

Created by **HARRY C. BJORKLUND** *Manufacturer*
3207 Girard Ave. No. - Minneapolis, Minn.

Ring Raiders
(68 diff.) (on
cards), 1990s
$5 per card

Multiple cards with rings were
issued

Rita Hayworth Photo
(see Real Photo)

Road Runner (see Looney
Tunes)

Robert E. Lee Flicker
Robert E. Lee face to soldier carrying a confederate flag. Must be part of a larger Civil War set

Robin (rubber) 1970s
$25-$50

Robin Logo Rec.
1980s (nestles)
$25-$50

Robin Logo (square)
1980s, $25-$50

Robin Hood Shoes (silver)
1950s (scarce) $175-$350

Robin Head (3D)
1980s (metal)(gold color)
$45-$90

Luminous rockets can be shot from barrel with the firing bar

Robin Logo (round)
1980s
$25-$50

Robin Hood
1970s (plastic)(silver)
$20-$35

Rocket-To-The-Moon
1951, (w/3 glow-in-dark rockets)
(gold & silver)(red top)(believe to be a Lone Ranger premium)
(complete) $600-$1200

HOW TO OPERATE
ROCKET-TO-THE-MOON RING

Here is your ROCKET-TO-THE-MOON RING, complete with 3 luminous plastic "rockets." You'll find it easy to operate and lots of fun, if you follow these directions. Rockets are luminous—they will glow brighter in the dark if you first expose them to a bright light.

LAUNCHING BARREL

FIRING BAR

CARRYING SLOT

...squeeze ring so that it fits snugly ... that it is adjustable in this ...

2. To cock the firing bar, push bar down as far as it will go, using thumb on one end and first finger on the other, pressing down equally on both ends. Then twist bar clockwise until it catches in the notches of launching barrel.

3. To insert "rocket," place "rocket" in launching barrel, with pointed end up and bottom resting snugly against firing bar.

4. To fire "rocket," trip firing bar by moving one end forward (as shown in picture above).

...ing is built to carry one "rocket" ...ncher when not in use (as ...picture above). To do this, ...cock firing bar and lock in ...(as in step 2 above). Then ..."rocket" into carrying slot, re-...the firing bar, and "rocket" ...is held securely in place.

Do a Friend a Good Turn or Get an Extra Ring for Yourself!

Give order blank below to your pal or to some other boy or girl so that they, too, can get a ROCKET-TO-THE-MOON RING.

"GOOD TURN" ORDER BLANK
Fill out and send at once.

KIX, Box 1085, Minneapolis, Minnesota

Please send me ____ ROCKET-TO-THE-MOON RING (S). For each one I enclose ____ in coin and a KIX box-top.

NAME _____

PLEASE PRINT

STREET _____

CITY _____ ZONE ____ STATE ____

Rockettes Flicker
1970s (oval, plastic)
$2-$5

Rockettes Flicker
1970s (round, plastic)
$2-$5

Rockettes Flicker
1960s (rectangle)
$5-$10

Rockettes Flicker
Rockettes dancing in a line.
1990s (modern "v" base)
$2-$5 ea.

Rocket Whistle
1953 (metal)
$20-$40

Rocky Figure
1993 (metal cloisonne)
$5-$10

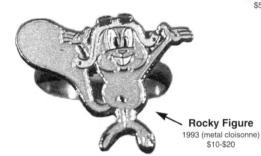

Rocky Figure
1993 (metal cloisonne)
$10-$20

Rocky Figure
1969 (metal cloisonne)
$10-$20

**Rocky &
Bullwinkle Paper**
1961 (vending machine)
(action rings purchased
from vending machines)
(in color)
$20-$35

BULLWINKLE & ROCKY
and HIS FRIENDS

©1961, P.A.T.
WARD PROD., IN

ACTION RINGS

Dudley Do-Right   Sherman   Peabody   Boris

**Rocky & Bulllwinkle
Flicker (1a)**
1961 (Boris)(side1)

**Rocky & Bullwinkle
Flicker (3a)**
1961 (Dudley) Side 1

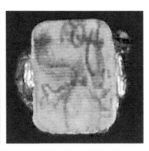

**Rocky & Bullwinkle
Flicker (4b)**
1961 (Mr. Peabody)
(side 2)(gold base)
$25-$50

**Rocky & Bullwinkle
Flicker (1b)**
1961 (Boris)(side 2)(gold base)
$25-$50

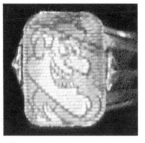

**Rocky & Bullwinkle
Flicker (3b)**
1961 (Dudley)((side 2)(gold base)
$25-$50

**Rocky & Bullwinkle
Flicker (5a)**
1961 (Rocky)
(side 1)(gold base)

**Rocky & Bullwinkle
Flicker (2)**
1961 (Bullwinkle) (gold base)
$25-$50

**Rocky & Bullwinkle
Flicker (4a)**
1961 (Mr. Peabody)
(side 1)(gold base)

**Rocky & Bullwinkle
Flicker (5b)**
1961 (Rocky)
(side 2)(gold base)
$25-$50

Name on base

Roger Wilco Flying Tiger
1940s
(w/metal whistle inside)
$115-$230

Metal whistle

Roger Wilco Rescue
1949
(w/metal whistle inside)
$75-$150

NOW BIGGER AND BETTER THAN EVER!

POWER HOUSE
MILK CHOCOLATE COVERED
CANDY BAR
BIG VALUE
GOOD EATING
MFG. BY WALTER H. JOHNSON CANDY CO. CHICAGO ILL.

ADVERTISED COAST TO COAST
IN SUNDAY COMICS

THRILLING!
EXCITING! SENSATIONAL
ROGER WILCO
Reg. Trade-Mark
RESCU
RING!
Never before—
anything like it!

THE ONLY RING WITH
3-WAY SIGNALLIN

SECRET ALARM
WHISTLE
in hidden chamber

BLUE MYSTERY LIG
glows in deepest dark

FLASHING REFLECT
sends real codes

Roger Wilco Rescue Paper
1949, $30-$60

Roger Wilco Magniray
1940s
$30-$60

Romper Room T.V.
(gold)
1960s
$50-$100

Romper Room T.V.
(silver)
1960s
$40-$80

**Rootie Kazootie T.V.
Flicker** 1950s
$75-$150

ROY ROGERS "King of the Cowboys"
says-

Here's a chance for you and your pals to
**GET EXTRA
"BRANDING IRON" RINGS**
with any one of your initials made
into a Western Brand!

STAR OF
REPUBLIC PICTURES

"Pardner, take your pick of these Western Brands so
you can 'brand' your schoolbooks, cap, balls, gloves,
and other belongin's with the initial of your first,
middle or last name.
"Look at the name under each brand and you can
tell how a cowpoke out on the range would read your
brand if he spotted it on a steer!"

Your Pardner,
Roy Rogers

*WHILE
SUPPLY LASTS*
ONLY 15¢
AND ONE BLUE STAR FROM
QUAKER OR MOTHER'S OATS PACKAGE

QUICK
QUAKER
OATS

QUICK
MOTHER'S
OATS

QUAKER AND MOTHER'S OATS
ARE THE SAME

**Rootie Kazootie
Lucky Spot**
1940s (rare)
$250-$500

Rosalie Gimple
1940s (gold color metal)(scarce)
$125-$250

**Roy Rogers Branding
Iron Paper**
1950s, $50-$60

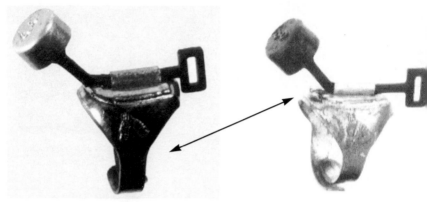

**Roy Rogers
Branding Iron**
(white cap), 1950s
$150-$300

**Roy Rogers
Branding Iron**
(black cap) 1950s
$100-$200

Roy Rogers Hat
1950s, (scarce)
$400-$800

Roy Rogers on horse
(oval) (silver), 1950s
$125-$250

Roy Rogers Saddle
1950s, $250-$500

Roy Rogers Microscope
(also see Sky King Magni-glo)
1950s, $50-$100

Roy Rogers on horse
(silver)
1950s, $125-$250

Roy Rogers Photo
(see Real Photos)

Roy Rogers Store
(silver metal), 1950s
$50-$100

Rudolph
1940s (metal)
$15-$30

Saddle, Smith Brothers
1940s
10-$25

Schlitz
1970s
$10-$20

Saddle (generic)
1950s (metal)
$10-$20

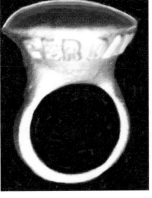

Salesman Door Knocker
1950 (large & heavy)
$50-$100

Sam The Sheep Dog (see Looney Tunes)

Scotty Flicker
1970s (metal, gold base)
(Hong Kong)
$5-$10

Saddle (generic)
1950s (metal)
$10-$20

San Francisco Expo
1939 (silver metal)
$30-$60

Sears Christmas Flicker
1960s (blue base)
$5-$10

Sears Christmas Flicker
1960s, "Sears has everything" picture
of four small trees to face of
Santa.(silver base)(2 versions)
$10-$20

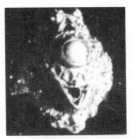

Secret Compartment
1960s (generic)
$10-$20

Secret Agent Lookaround
1930s (Brass w/same base as R.O.A.
Mystic Eye & Lone Ranger National
Defenders) (Very rare)
(a proto-type)
$250-$500

Shadow
1994 (gold w/diamond inset)(25 produced)
(Diamond Comic Distr.)(numbered)
$750

**Secret
Compartment**
(generic)
1950s, $10-$20

Shadow
1994 (silver)(Diamond Comic Distr.)
(numbered)
$200

HERE IS YOUR *Shadow* RING
PRESENTED WITH THE 'blue coal'
COMPLIMENTS OF

INSTRUCTIONS FOR "CHARGING" YOUR RING
SO THAT IT WILL GLOW IN THE DARK

To charge your "Shadow" Ring so that it will glow in the darkness. hold it close to a lighted electric bulb for a half minute or more. The longer you hold the ring to the light. the longer and brighter it will glow. And you may recharge it as often as you wish. The ring can also be charged by holding it in the sunlight. BUT DO NOT EXPOSE THE RING TO THE DIRECT RAYS OF THE SUN FOR TOO LONG!

TO MAKE YOUR RING LARGER

(1) Put the ring in hot water (not boiling hot) for about five minutes. (2) Take it out of the water and gently bend it until it fits your finger. (3) After bending it to the correct size. put it in cold water for one minute.

YOU ARE NOW A MEMBER OF THE SHADOW "STOP CRIME" CLUB

(See other side for special order blank)

YOU ARE NOW
A MEMBER OF
The Shadow
"STOP-CRIME" CLUB

Shadow Blue Coal Paper

USE THIS BLANK TO ORDER ADDITIONAL
Shadow RINGS

If you want to order additional "Shadow" Rings for your own use or for gifts, send the order blank below to: "The Shadow", P.O. Box No. 5, Madison Square Station, New York City. Simply enclose 10c for each ring you order.

Please send me _____ rings. Enclosed is _____ cents

NAME _____

Print Name and Address

ADDRESS _____

CITY _____   STATE _____

THIS OFFER EXPIRES DECEMBER 31st, 1941

Katharine Hoffman
111 E. Market St.
Williamstown, Pa.

Plastic top resembling a chunk of blue coal

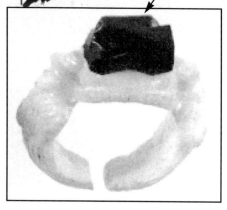

Shadow Blue Coal Ring
(glows-in-dark), 1941(plastic)(blue top resembling a chunk of coal)
$275-$550

Shadow Blue Coal Envelope
(see previous page for price)

Shadow Carey Salt
(black stone)
(glows-in-dark), 1947
(also see Buck Rogers Ring of Saturn, Jack Armstrong Dragon Eye & Shadow Blue Coal)
$500-$1000

Shelly Winters (see
Movie Star Photo)

Shield
1930s (metal)(generic)
$25-$45

Shield
1930s (metal)(generic)
$25-$45

Shirley Temple
1930s (metal)(scarce)
$300-$500

Shmoo Luck Rings
on card
1950s
$30-$60 ea.
card w/rings - $500

Shmoo ring
enlarged

Shoe Shine
(gumball), 1950s
$20-$40

Sir Ector
(see Sword in the Stone)

Sitting Bull (plastic)
1950s (Kelloggs)
$10-$20

Skeezix (see Post Tin)

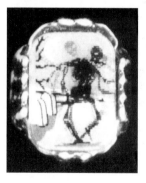

Skeleton Flicker
dancing skeleton in a graveyard
moving back & forth
$10-$20

Signet (generic)(ad in Showcase Comics #26, 5-6/60)
Ring price $20-$40

Skull
(gold w/red eyes)
1939
$50-$100

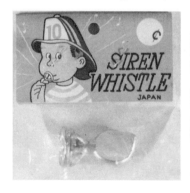

Siren Whistle in package
(elephant base) (gold & silver versions),
1930s
$30 complete in bag

Siren Whistle
(not in package)
$12-$25

Skeleton Rings
(Boxed set), 1990s
$30 complete in box

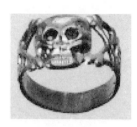

Skull, Popsicle
(red eye) (silver)
1940s
$50-$100

Sky Bar Pilot
1940s (metal)
$150-$300

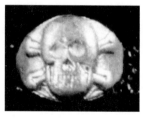

Skull (foreign)
1950s (2 diff.)
$50-$100

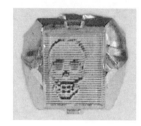

Skull Flicker
1960s (silver base)
$15-$25

Sky Bird
1940s (metal)
$75-$150

Skull, Montrose
Lucky
1940s
$50-$100

Tastes so fresh
because it's
just
60 seconds old
when you open the jar!

Be sure Mom always has plenty
of fresh-tasting Peter Pan
Peanut Butter around!

Use this coupon to order more Rings!
SKY KING, Box 3636, Dept. O, Chicago 77, Ill.

Dear Sky: Please send me (state number) ____ Sky King Aztec Emerald
Calendar Ring(s). For each one I enclose 20¢ plus a 3¢ stamp to help cover the cost of
handling, and a piece torn from a Peter Pan Peanut Butter jar label.

Name _____

**Skull, Pirate,
Carribean**
(Disney), 1980s
$10-$20

Sky King Aztec paper
(Scarce)(complete)
(see next page)

Here's your Sky King

AZTEC EMERALD CALENDAR RING

...isn't it a beauty?

Aztec Fire God — the sinister pagan god of fire and sacrifice that all the Aztecs feared!

Sparkling emerald green plastic stone!

Genuine 24-karat gold plated!

> **Sky King Aztec Emerald calendar Ring Paper**
> (scarce)
> $100-$125

Adjusts to any size finger!

Silver-plated stone mounting!

Ancient Aztec calendar—looks just like the one Sky King deciphered to find the clues to the hidden Aztec treasure!

Get another Ring for yourself or a friend! See other side

Sky King Aztec Emerald Calendar Ring
1940s, $450-$900

Here's your
Sky King *ELECTRONIC TELEVISION Picture RING*
.... and here's how to use it:

To make Sky King's picture glow in the dark like a real television image, hold ring to a light, then take it into a dark place. Picture will actually glow electronically through the Television Viewer Screen which magnifies image.

Secret Compartment for hiding messages! Just lift up Television Viewer Screen and slip message in.

To make pictures of Clipper, Penny, Jim and Martha appear like magic, cut dotted lines on the blank strips. Then rub the squares with the "presto" pad dipped in water. Then trim the pictures to fit in the ring.

Detecto-scope built into ring magnifies 2 times! Use it for detecting fingerprints or decoding tiny secret messages

REMIND MOM TO HAVE PLENTY OF PETER PAN PEANUT BUTTER AROUND—IT'S SKY KING'S FAVORITE!

Now there are *two* delicious kinds of Peter Pan—smooth Peter Pan in the red top jar, and Peter Pan inchy Peanut Butter in the green top jar. And if i want another ring, send a round aluminum disc the paper liner from under a Peter Pan Peanut ter jar top and 15c for each Television Picture ig you want together with your name and address Sky King, Box 3636, Chicago 77, Illinois.

Sky King Electronic Television Picture Ring Paper
1940s
$30-$40

Sky King Electronic Television Picture
1940s (metal)(w/photos)
$100-$200

SEE Sky King's picture glowing through the **TELEVISION VIEWER SCREEN!**
Magnifies picture 2 times...looks like a real Television Screen!

Get it Kids! Nothing like it before! **SKY KING'S**

ELECTRONIC TELEVISION PICTURE RING

Has SECRET COMPARTMENT inside for hiding messages!

ELECTRONIC-GLO PICTURE of Sky King set in ring glows in the dark, like a real television image! Actually works electronically—you "charge" the picture by holding it up to a light, forcing the electrons out of their normal position. In the dark, the electrons return to their normal position, giving off light. It will amaze you and your friends!

EXTRA PICTURES WORK LIKE MAGIC—pictures of Clipper, Penny, Martha and Jim Bell that you can wear in the ring! They're amazing—they come blank, but when you rub them with the wet "presto" pad, pictures appear like magic! They fit right into the ring, so you can have a different picture on every day!

DETECTO-SCOPE is built right into ring—magnifies 2 times for detecting finger-prints or secret writing!

It's the most amazing ring ever! Think of it—the magnified Electronic-Glo Picture of Sky King actually glows in the dark, like a real television image! This ring *looks* like a real television set, too, with its magnifying Television Viewer Screen. And you get four different Magic Picture Settings to wear in the ring, too—you can wear a different one every day. There's just never been anything like Sky King's Electronic Television Picture Ring before!

A real beauty—made of strong gold-like metal, with big Television Viewer Screen. Fits any size finger.

Easy to get—just follow the simple instructions. Send for yours *today*, while this amazing offer lasts!

There are two kinds of Peter Pan Peanut Butter—smooth Peter Pan sandwich the red jar top, and Peter Pan Crunchy Peanut Butter with the green jar top. You can send in the disc or liner from *either kind* of Peter Pan for your Television Picture Ring.

Send for your Ring TODAY! Only 15¢ with one disc or liner from inside

PETER PAN Peanut Butter jar (THIS OFFER GOOD ONLY in U.S.A.)

Listen to my air adventures! Hear how the Electronic Television Picture Ring helps me solve exciting adventure mysteries! For plenty of thrills, tune in "The Adventures of Sky King," every other weekday evening, 5:30 to 6:00 on your local ABC station.

Sky King

Dear Sky — With this coupon I am sending 15¢ and one round aluminum disc or the paper jar top liner from inside a Peter Pan Peanut Butter jar, for *my* Sky King's Electronic Television Picture Ring. (Note: If you want more than one ring, send one disc or liner and 15¢ for each Electronic Television Picture Ring you want.)

PRINT NAME AND ADDRESS PLAINLY IN PENCIL

NAME _____

STREET ADDRESS _____

CITY _____ ZONE ____ STATE ____

Mail to SKY KING, BOX 3636, CHICAGO 77, ILLINOIS

SEND this coupon TODAY!

Sky King Electronic Television Paper
1940s (see previous page for price)

Sky King Kaleidoscope Ring
Aluminum tube with viewing lens. Multiple images of Sky King can be seen inside while rotating the tube. The base is gold finished brass attached to a black metal saddle holding the tube. A very rare prototype ring.

Sky King Kaleidoscope
1940s (prototype, metal)(very rare)
Fine - $6500
Near Mint - $9000

Here's Your Sky King Magni-Glow Writing Ring from Peter Pan

. . . and here's how to use it:

Secret Stratospheric Pen in ring writes at any altitude, or under water, in red ink!

Built-in Detecto-Scope magnifying glass for detecting fingerprints or decoding messages!

Mysterious Glo-Signaler gives a strange green light! You can send blinker signals with it!

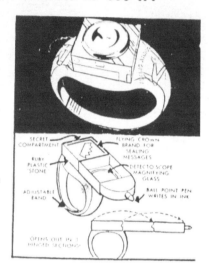

Remember to have mom get some more Peter Pan Peanut Butter—it's Sky King's Favorite.

Now there two delicious kinds of Peter Pan to choose from. Smooth Peter Pan in the red top jar and in the green top jar Peter Pan Crunchy Peanut Butter.

Sky King Magni-Glo Writing
$30-$40

Sky King Magni-Glo Writing Ring
Opens in three hinged sections. Contains a secret compartment & magnifying glass hidden in a ruby red base. At night coded eerie green blinker light pulses can be sent.

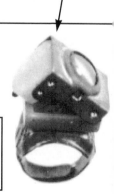

Sky King Magni-glo Writing
1940s (also see Roy Rogers Microscope)
$50-$100

Sky King Magni-Glo Writing Paper
1940s, $10-$20

Sky King Mystery Picture Ring Ad
1940s
$10-$20

How to use your amazing
SKY KING'S MYSTERY PICTURE RING
—brought to you by Peter Pan Peanut Butter

See Sky King in disguise

—the one he used to break up the gang of crooks in the thrilling radio adventure! Place your finger alongside the ring where the round gray disc overlaps the edge of the ring. Slowly revolve the disc — and Sky King's picture appears! Revolve it again, and Sky King will reappear in the disguise he wore when he broke up the gang. It's thrilling, amazing, mysterious!

For even clearer pictures, slip off stone and hold it to light

Glows mysteriously in the dark! Sky King's Mystery Picture Ring gives off a strange green glow in the dark! Use it for making secret signals at night — identifying friends — guiding "convoys" in the dark!

Brand secret messages! Slide the stone off your ring ... then press the top of the ring on sealing wax or candle wax. Leaves the same brand Sky King used! Use it for your own special signature!

Hide messages in secret compartment! Slide the stone off your ring and you'll find a hidden compartment for carrying important messages, codes, etc. where no one will find them!

SECRET MEETING TODAY 4 PM

Be sure every member of your gang has **SKY KING'S** Mystery Picture Ring!

Don't miss "The Adventures of Sky King" on your local ABC station **5:30 to 6:00** every other weekday evening

DO THIS NOW: For each Mystery Picture Ring you want member of your gang do this: mail the coupon, with 15c and metal band cut from inside the Peter Pan Peanut Butter

Name _____
Your date _____
City _____ Zone _____ State _____

Mail to: SKY KING, BOX 3636, CHICAGO 77, I

Sky King Mystery Picture Ring Paper
1940s, $50-$75

Sky King Mystery Picture
1940s (scarce)
$300-$700

Kids! Get Sky King's mysterious
NAVAJO TREASURE RING

plus a handy
present for Mom –

Send only 10¢

King's mysterious
ajo Treasure Ring—
like the one Sky found bear
he mysterious clues that
ed him find the long-lost
o turquoise mine! A strong
beautiful Ring in genuine
o Indian design, with a sky blue stone that looks like
turquoise set in gleaming silver-like metal. The myste-
centuries old Navajo symbols on the sides are the
Sky King deciphered to reveal the whereabouts of
abulous lost Navajo mine! A Ring you'll be proud to
that your friends will envy! Order yours today! Fits
ze finger.

For You!

For Mom!

dy Plastic Re-Seal Jar Cap—
ay on tight, but easy to remove, cover for
Pan Peanut Butter Jars. Turns empty
Pan or other drinking glasses into valu-
food savers. You get this Re-Seal Jar Cap
Mom at no extra cost with every Navajo
sure Ring you order for yourself— you get
Send only 10 cents! Order today!

Don't miss my
radio adventures—
fun, thrills, and adven-
tures galore on "The
Adventures of Sky
King" every other
weekday evening,
5:30 to 6:00, on your
local ABC station.

(signed)
Sky King

**Special for
Peter Pan Peanut Butter users!**
Just send your name, address,
and 10¢ — that's all! You will
receive a beautiful Navajo
Treasure Ring for yourself, plus
a present for Mom—a handy
plastic Re-Seal Cap for Peter
Pan Peanut Butter!

Buy a jar of Peter Pan
Send this coupon today!

Dear Sky King —

Please send me (circle number)—Navajo Treasure Rings with each Ring comes a
Plastic Pete-Pan Peanut-Butter Re-Seal Jar Cap for Mom) for each Ring I enclose 10¢.
Note: This offer good only in U.S.A. and expires June 30, 1950.
Print name and address plainly in pencil.

Name _____

Street address _____

City _____ Zone _____ State _____

Mail to Sky King, Box 3636, Dept. O, Chicago 77, Illinois
NOTE: If you want the Plastic Jar Cap and not the Ring, just
send your name, address with no money to above address.

**Sky King Navajo
Treasure Ring Ad**
1950s
$10-$20

**Sky King
Navajo Treasure Ring**
1950s (silver color metal base)
(turquoise colored stone)

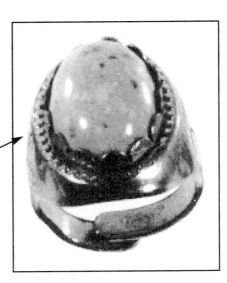

Sky King Navajo Treasure Ring
1950s (blue stone)(Advertised on back cover of
Danger Trail comic book #1, 1950)
$100-$200

"Hey kids! Here's your Sky King Radar Signal Ring !!"

Makes mysterious symbols!

Place any cut-out symbol on stone, and hold stone up to bright light. Remove the cut-out, and the symbol will appear on the stone in the dark!

Stone glows in the dark!

Makes a mysterious bluish light! And to make it glow even brighter, hold stone close to bright electric light before taking it into a dark place!

Sky King's own insignia

—the Winged Propeller—appears on each side of the ring!

Band is simulated gold!

Handsome, gold-like finish. Looks and sparkles like real gold! Bright, long-lasting.

Stone is removable!

To remove it, just slip it sideways.

Secret compartment!

In underside of stone. For secret messages, codes, etc. Nobody would suspect it was there!

Flying Crown Brand insignia

Appears when stone is removed. By pressing it on sealing wax, candle wax, you leave the mark of the Flying Crown Brand. Use it for sealing private letters, secret club papers, etc.

Ring fits any size finger!

Band can be adjusted to fit you perfectly.

Sky King Radar Paper
1940s, $30-$40

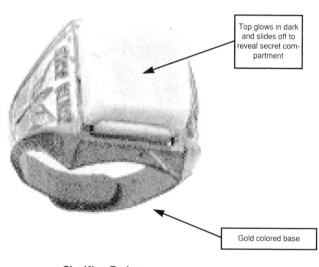

Top glows in dark and slides off to reveal secret compartment

Gold colored base

Sky King Radar
1940s (metal)
$75-$150

**Sky King Tele-Blinker
Ring Paper**
1950s, $20-$30

Telescope extends for
viewing distant objects.
3-power magnification

uminous blinker and
a clicking sound is
activated by pushing
top up and down

Sky King Teleblinker
1950s (metal)
$75-$150

Here's your Sky King 2-WAY TELE-BLINKER RING
and here's how to use it

to send signals . . .

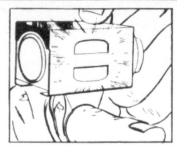

1. Place the ring on your trigger finger with windows facing out.

2. Push metal box down. The blinker will appear bright enough to be seen for at least 70 feet—and for night signaling, it glows in the dark. When you release the pressure, the blinker snaps up again to the "off" position. Notice also that when you signal there is a clicking sound like a telegraph key so that you can send sound signals when you can't be seen—or even over the phone.

3. Make dots or dashes by pushing the box down quickly for dots and slowly for dashes. There is a short "action" code on top the tele-blinker Or you can use the Morse Code below.

A	·—	F	··—·	K	—·—	P	·——·	U	··—
B	—···	G	——·	L	·—··	Q	——·—	V	···—
C	—·—·	H	····	M	——	R	·—·	W	·——
D	—··	I	··	N	—·	S	···	X	—··—
E	·	J	·———	O	———	T	—	Y	—·——
								Z	——··

to receive signals

Just pull out the jointed 3-power telescope and watch your partner's tele-blinker flash messages to you in dots and dashes. You can use your tele-blinker to view distant objects also.

flashes recognition signal

On the opposite side from the two windowed tele-blinker, Sky King's Flying Crown brand appears when you press the top of the ring Release it and it disappears.

Remind Mom to Have Plenty of Peter Pan Peanut Butter on Hand
—It Is Sky King's Favorite!

There are two delicious kinds of Peter Pan—smooth Peter Pan in the red top jar and Peter Pan crunchy in the green top jar

To get another 2-WAY TELE-BLINKER RING, send the round aluminum disk°or the paper liner from under a Peter Pan peanut butter jar top and 25c together with your name and address to SKY KING, Box 3636, Dept. D, Chicago 77, Ill. (Good only in U.S.A Expires March 13, 1950)

Sky King
Tele-Blinker paper
1950s $50-$60

Walt Disney's Sleeping Beauty
WITH REMOVABLE SWORD
OFFICIAL PRINCE PHILLIP RING

WALT DISNEY PRODUCTIONS
HIMMEL SONS - NEW YORK, N. Y.

Sleeping Beauty Ring paper
1960s, $15-$20

Smilin' Jack (see Canada Dry & Post Tin)

Sliding Whistle
(see Tom Mix--)

**Sleeping Beauty
Prince Phillip**
(hard plastic) (Disney)
(also see weapon)
1960s
$20-$40

**Smith Brothers
Air Force**
(Cough Drops), 1940s
$40-$80

Smith Brothers
Marine (Cough Drops)
1940s
$40-$80

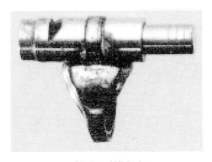

Sliding Whistle
(generic), 1940s (rare
$150-$250

Smith Brothers
Navy (Cough Drops)
1940s
$40-$80

Smith Brothers Saddle
(see Saddle)

Smitty (see Post Tin)

Smokey Bear
1990s (2 diff.)
$1

Smokey Stover
(see Post Tin)

Smurfs
1980s (2 diff.)
$10-$20 ea.

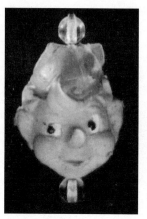

Crackle
(red hat) (rubber)
$150-$300

Pop
(yellow hat) (rubber)
$300-$600

Snoopy & Woodstock
1980s (metal cloisonne)
$10-$20

Snap
(white hat) (rubber)
$250-$500

Snap, Crackle, & Pop
(3 ring set), Kelloggs, 1950s
(rare) (priced above)

Sneezy Mouse (see Looney Tunes)

Snoopy (see Lucy)

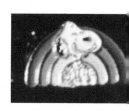

Snoopy
1980s (metal)
$10-$20

Snoopy
1980s (metal cloisonne)
$10-$20

Snoopy
1980s (metal cloisonne)
$10-$20

Snow White & 7 Dwarfs
1990s (in color, metal)
(Sleepy)
$1-$2

Snuffy Smith (see Post Tin)

Soccer Flicker
1960s (gold base metal
(Hong Kong)
$4-$8

Soupy Sales Flicker
1960s (silver base)(side 1)
$15-$25

Snoopy on Bike
1980s (metal cloisonne)
$10-$20

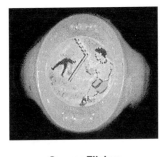

Soccer Flicker
1960s (red & blue base versions)
$4-$8

Soupy Sales Flicker
"Soupy Sales" to picture of Soupy
with fingers touching his head.
(1960s)(silver base)(side 2)
$15-$25

Snow White & 7 Dwarfs
1930s (brass metal painted)
(Doc)
$50-$100

Soccer Flicker
1960s (gold base metal)
(Hong Kong)
$4-$8

Space
1960s (plastic),. $10-$20

Space (see Apollo)

Snow White & 7 Dwarfs
1980s (metal cloisonne)
(Happy), $10-$20

Space Rings
1960s (vending machine paper)
(in color)(scarce)
$15-$25

Space (plastic)
1960s (10 diff.) (vending machine)
$5-$10 ea.

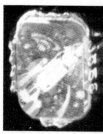

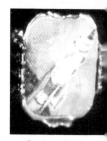

Space Flicker
Outerspace scene with rocket
to farther view of ship with Sa
in background (1960s)
$15-$30

Space Flicker
Rocket ship ready to take off
rocket ship taking off 1960s
$15-$30

**Space Patrol
Compass**
(gold & silver versions)
1950s
$75-$150

Space Patrol Cosmic Glc
1950s (plastic)(red & blue)
$400-$800

Who is it?

Buzz Corry?

One of the Gang?

... Could be YOU!

Wear this official

SPACE PATROL OUTER SPACE HELMET

can see out . . . but nobody can see in . . . because
ystic Strato-Viewer that SPACE PATROLLERS
. . . Fresh-air oxygen tubes printed right on helmet
Solar golden color!

Keeps your identity a secret!

et yours, send only 25¢ (no stamps, please) and 1
top from any one of these Ralston cereals: Wheat
, Rice Chex, Regular or Instant Ralston, with your
and address to Outer Space Helmet, Box 987,
ouis, Mo.

s good only in U.S.A. and may be withdrawn at any
Void wherever prohibited or restricted.

Talk about fast action,
Space Patrollers! . . .

this COSMIC

ROCKET LAUNCHER

has got it!

Slick red and yellow plastic rocket with an unbreakable
snap-on scout car! Stainless steel launching gun sends
rocket whooshing over 33 feet of special breakproof
nylon cord! Scout car drops down at end of trip! Use
it for window-to-window communications with a pal next
door . . . special place inside scout car for secret
messages!

To get yours, send only 25¢ (no stamps, please) and 1
box top from any one of these Ralston cereals: Wheat
Chex, Rice Chex, Regular or Instant Ralston, with your
name and address to Cosmic Rocket Launcher, Box 987,
St. Louis, Mo.

Look like a space
stranger! Wear a

MAN-FROM-MARS

TOTEM HEAD

**with Magic
Forehead Vision!**

Makes you look just like the space
men Commander Corry found on
Mars! . . . You can see in! . . . One face on front,
another on back . . . Order for your
whole gang. Stack several up and
make a TOTEM POLE!

To get yours, send only 25¢ (no
stamps, please) and 1 box top from
any one of these Ralston cereals:
Wheat Chex, Rice Chex, Regular or
Instant Ralston, with your name and
address to Totem Head, Box 987,
St. Louis, Mo.

How to use your Hydrogen Ray Gun
Ring that lets you

WATCH ATOMS BEING SPLIT!

FIRING CAP

ATOMIC
CHAMBER

OBSERVATION
LENS

1. Take your ring into a real
   dark room.

2. Wait until your eyes get
   used to the dark—about
   1 to 2 minutes.

3. Slide the Firing Cap off the
   back of the ring.

4. Hold the ring close to one
   eye, and look through the
   Observation Lens.

5. See the bouncing dots and
   flashes of light in the Atom
   Chamber! That's atomic
   power in action—the
   energy released by atoms
   as they're split!

PRINTED IN U.S.A.

**Tell your gang how to get a
Hydrogen Ray Gun Ring!**

For each Ring, send only 25¢ in
coin (no stamps, please) and 1 box
top from any one of these Ralston
Cereals: Wheat Chex, Rice Chex,
Regular or Instant Ralston, with
your name and address to Hydrogen Ray Gun Ring, Box 987, St.
Louis, Mo.

Space Patrol Hydrogen Ray Gun paper
(scarce)(both sides illustrated), $125-$150

ek through back of ring
a dark room and Watch
atoms being split

**pace Patrol Hydrogen
Ray Gun**
1950s
$150-$300

Space Patrol Printing
1950s
w/stamp pad
$300-$500
Ring only - $150-$200

Space Ring (on card)
(sparkles like meteor dust)
(rings in various colors) (plastic) 1950s
Set-$150

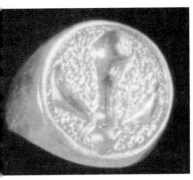

Spawn (Image Comics)
(1993) (silver & gold
versions exist)
Silver -$250
Gold w/diamond - $1000

Spiderman (gold)
1993, (limited to 12)(Marvel Ent. Group)
Near Mint - $3,000

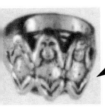

Speak No Evil
(3 monkeys) (metal)
1950s, $10-$20

Speedy Gonzales
1970s (hand painted)(also see Looney Tunes)
$6-$12

Spiderman (bronze)
1993 (limited to 50)(Marvel Ent. Group)
Near Mint - $400

Spider (pulp character)
(pulp & theater giveaway)(scarce), 1930s (silver
base)(less than 20 known)Good - $2500
Very Good - $3750
Fine - $5000
Very Fine - $7500
Near Mint - $10,000

Red spider over
black top

Spiderman (silver)
1993, (limited to 50)(Marvel Ent. Group)
Near Mint - $600

Spiderman
1994 (Marvel Ent. Group)(1200 minted)
Near Mint - $75

Stanley Club (radio)
(green stone, gold metal)
1940s
$150-$300

Spiderman Face
(green), 1980s (Marvel Ent. Group)
(see Marvel)(green top, white base)
$30-$60

Stapuff Marshmellow
1980s (metal)(2 views of
same ring)
$15-$25

Spiderman (vitamins)
1960s (metal)(Marvel Ent. Group)
$50-$100

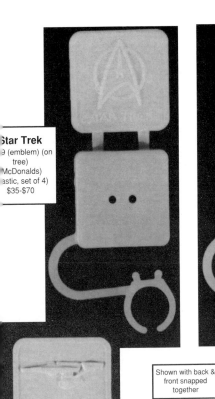

Star Trek
9 (emblem) (on
tree)
McDonalds)
astic, set of 4)
$35-$70

Star Trek
(Kirk) (on tree)
(McDonalds)
(plastic, 4 diff.),
1979
$35-$70

Shown with back &
front snapped
together

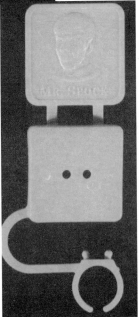

Star Trek
1979 (Enterprise) (on tree)
(McDonalds) (plastic, set of 4),
$35-$70

Star Trek
(Mr. Spock)(McDonalds, plastic)
1979 (set of 4)
$35-$70

Star Trek
1979 (Mr. Spock) (on tree)
(McDonalds) (plastic, set of 4)
$35-$70

R2D2

Darth Vader

C3PO

Star Wars
1977 (set of 3)
$15-$20 ea.

Star Wars (set in box) 1977 $40-$80

Star Wars (8 diff.),
(C3PO, Fighter, Force (lg.),
Force (sm.), R2D2,
Vader, Xfighter, Yoda),
1980s
$7-$15 ea.

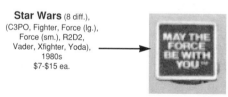

Starriors
1984 (on card)(2 rings)
(Includes comic book)
$50 complete set

Starriors
(came on card)
(2 diff.), 1984, came with
comic book
$20 ea.

Steer Head Ring
1940s (generic)
$75-$150

Straight Arrow Face Ring
1950s
$25-$50

Straight Arrow Gold Arrow Instructions
1940s (rare, less than 10 known)
$200-$250

Story Book Ring
1960s, $50-$125

Straight Arrow Gold Arrow Ring
(Bandana slide)
1940s
$25-$50

Lens magnifies photo of Straight Arrow in cave

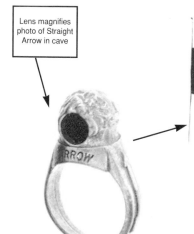

Straight Arrow Golden Nugget Ring
1940s
w/photo inside (see Golden Nugget Cave)
$125-$250

Here's **your STRAIGHT ARROW**

GOLDEN NUGGET *Secret Picture* **RING.**

SEE THE INSIDE OF MY SECRET CAVE
There you will find your picture with my Palomino, Fury, and me!
Straight Arrow

This sensational Golden Nugget Secret Picture Ring is an official emblem of the Straight Arrow Tribe. Be sure to wear it at all times, to identify yourself to other tribe members.

Tell all your friends and fellow tribesmen about this wonderful new ring. Make sure they get theirs right away. Coupon on the reverse side tells how!

Handy coupon on back for a friend!

Straight Arrow Golden Nugget Paper
1940s, (rare) $150-$200

HURRY! SHORT TIME OFFER!

NABISCO SHREDDED WHEAT

BOX 113, DEPT. R, NEW YORK 46, N. Y.

Please rush me my STRAIGHT ARROW GOLDEN NUGGET PICTURE RING. I enclose 25¢, a NABISCO SHREDDED WHEAT Box Top, and a snapshot of the person whose picture I want in the ring.

(Please Print)

NAME

ADDRESS

CITY   ZONE   STATE

No stamps please. Offer good in U. S. only, for a limited time.

NATIONAL BISCUIT COMPANY

LISTEN TO THE EXCITING STRAIGHT ARROW RADIO PROGRAM ON MBS – LOOK IN YOUR PAPER FOR TIME AND STATION.

IMPORTANT! Do not send negatives, valuable or framed pictures or any pictures larger than a post card. Allow at least three weeks for delivery.

THE BREAKFAST FULL OF POWER FROM NIAGARA FALLS

Straight Arrow Golden Nugget Paper
(rare)(priced w/above)

Sunbeam Bread Flicker
1950s, Sunbeam Bread Girl holding piece of bread to her eating the piece of bread.
$10-$20

Strawberry Shortcake
1980s (metal)
$15-$25

Sundial Shoes
1940s (see Fireball Twigg)
$30-$60

Super F-87 Jet Plane Paper
(1948)(page 1)(Scarce), $100-$125

HOW TO BE A CHAMP PILOT WITH YOUR "F-87" SUPER JET PLANE:

YOUR FIRST TAKE-OFF. Your Super Jet Plane comes to you all set to fly. Just slip the ring on your finger — with nose of plane pointing away from you. Aim it. Then press down quickly with finger nail on the Secret Launching Trigger — located to the right of the plane. Zoom! Away your plane streaks — (Be sure to hold trigger down until plane is launched to avoid tail surfaces striking trigger or finger.)

GET READY TO RE-LAUNCH! To replace plane on your ring, simply slide the hollow tail of your plane over the launching pin on the ring. Push plane back gently until it "clicks" in place. Zoom 'er again!

ENGINE TROUBLE? If you have a little difficulty launching your plane, examine your launching pin. It may be bent down too far. If so, bend it slightly upwards.

WIN DISTANCE RACES! You and your friends will want to race your jet planes. So here's how to get the *most distance* from *your* plane. Make repeated test flights at different launching angles until you discover which angle lets your plane fly the *farthest*. **Find the Proper Launching Angle** Then always launch your plane from this angle.

WIN LANDING CONTESTS!

It's fun to pretend you're landing your plane on a carrier. But it's tricky to do it right. Cut a piece of paper in the shape of a carrier 12 inches long, 3 inches wide. Place this cut-out carrier on the floor or a table. Then practice coming in *low* and *slow* — *not high or fast*. With practice, you can become an expert "flat top" flyer.

ZOOM THE LOOP!

Here's a trick that will amaze your friends — but it takes practice! Make a loop of wire about 12 inches across. Hang this loop from a lightcord or low tree branch about 5 feet above the ground. Then practice zooming your plane through the loop — close to it at first, then farther away.

Do not point jet plane at yourself or anyone else!

WIN "DOGFIGHTS"!

It's fun to "dogfight" your jet planes — and here's how to do it: First, your friend will zoom his plane into the air. Then, you "shoot him down" from the side with your plane. If you miss, he gets a chance to shoot at your plane. Here's a tip: aim ahead of the plane — *not at it*.

BOOM THE BALLOON!

Blow up a toy balloon and tie it to a lightcord or low tree branch. Let it swing back and forth — then zoom your plane at it. BOOM! If you miss, your friend gets a chance to zoom it.

Tip: When the balloon is swinging, always shoot ahead of it — not at it. Aim at the center of the balloon — not at the top or bottom.

GET YOUR FRIENDS TO FORM A SUPER JET PLANE RING SQUADRON!

Super F-87 Jet Plane
Kellogg's ad for ring
$5-$10

Secret launching trigger when pressed zooms plane away. Plane can be reloaded by sliding over the launching pin until it clicks in place.

Kellogg's Corn Flakes box top premium. Plane and ring base should be displayed in un-cocked position to preserve the launching spring.

Superman Ring
(In box w/clear top & full color
paper display) (3 diff.)
1970s
$30 ea.

Super F-87 Jet Plane
1948 (offered on Superman radio &
other shows)(shoots plastic
plane; spring loaded)(previously
believed to be a Superman premium)
$125-$250

**Superman
Figure**
1990s
$2

Superman Crusader
(silver metal) 1940s
$125-$250

Superman Emblem
1990s
$1

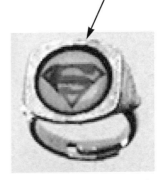

Superman Emblem
(blue logo) (Nestle)
1980, $25-$50

Superman Emblem
1993 (sold at Warner Bros. stores)
$50 complete in box

Nestlé milk chocolate

Nestlé
milk chocolate

net wt 1¹⁄₁₆ oz

Nestlé milk chocolate

Real Chocolate

FREE SUPERMAN RING
WITH 10 WRAPPERS

FREE SUPERMAN RING* —Yours for only 10 complete wrappers from any
brand of Nestlé single bars* (or 5 wrappers plus $1.50 check or money
order only please). On a separate piece of paper print your name, address
and zip code, send it with the wrappers to
NESTLÉ, P.O. Box 5455, MAPLE PLAIN, MN 55348.

"NESTLÉ CRUNCH" NESTLÉ MILK CHOCOLATE NESTLÉ CHOCOLITE" NESTLÉ $100,000" BAR
NO MINIATURE BAR WRAPPERS PLEASE. ALLOW UP TO 8 WEEKS FOR SHIPMENT. OFFER GOOD ONLY IN U.S.A. VOID WHERE PROHIBITED.
OFFER EXPIRES DECEMBER 31, 1979. ® SUPERMAN AND THE S INSIGNIA ARE TRADEMARKS OF DC COMICS INC. 1944

INGREDIENTS MILK CHOCOLATE (SUGAR FRESH WHOLE MILK
COCOA BUTTER CHOCOLATE LIQUOR LECITHIN — AN EMULS
VANILLIN — AN ARTIFICIAL FLAVORI')
PREPARED BY THE NESTLE COMP   INC WHIT'

No 1316-4   NESTLÉ

Superman Emblem paper wrapper
Nestle , 1980s
$50-$60

Superman Emblem
1970s (movie)(metal)
$25-$50

Superman Emblem
1990s
$2-$5

Superman Flicker
1960s (8 diff.)
(scarce)
$100-$200 ea.

© NATIONAL
PERIODICAL
PUBLICATIONS, Inc.

Get
your
official
SUPERMAN
ACTION
RING
here

Superman Flicker Paper
(1960s, from vending machine)(rare)
$60-$125

Superman Magnetic Kryptonite Ring
ring only - $15-$30

Superman Magnetic Kryptonite Ring
(plastic, Green top)(came in box with Superman figure.
Magnetic ring will push Superman down)
1990 (front of package)
$50 complete in package

Superman Magnetic Kryptonite Ring
1990 (back of package)
$50 complete in package

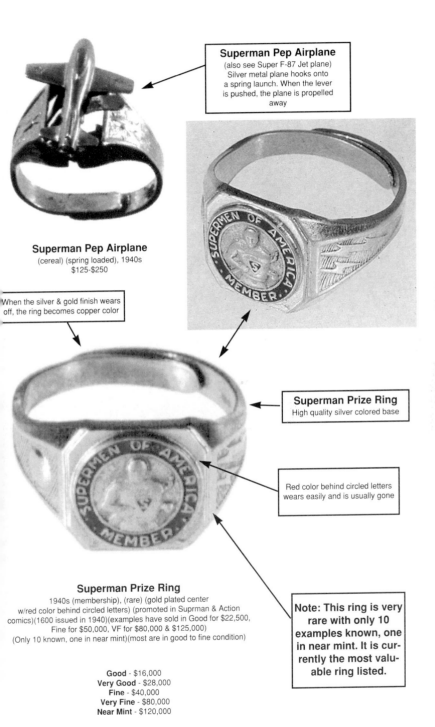

Superman Pep Airplane
(also see Super F-87 Jet plane)
Silver metal plane hooks onto
a spring launch. When the lever
is pushed, the plane is propelled
away

Superman Pep Airplane
(cereal) (spring loaded), 1940s
$125-$250

When the silver & gold finish wears
off, the ring becomes copper color

Superman Prize Ring
High quality silver colored base

Red color behind circled letters
wears easily and is usually gone

Superman Prize Ring
1940s (membership), (rare) (gold plated center
w/red color behind circled letters) (promoted in Suprman & Action
comics)(1600 issued in 1940)(examples have sold in Good for $22,500,
Fine for $50,000, VF for $80,000 & $125,000)
(Only 10 known, one in near mint)(most are in good to fine condition)

Note: This ring is very
rare with only 10
examples known, one
in near mint. It is cur-
rently the most valu-
able ring listed.

Good - $16,000
Very Good - $28,000
Fine - $40,000
Very Fine - $80,000
Near Mint - $120,000

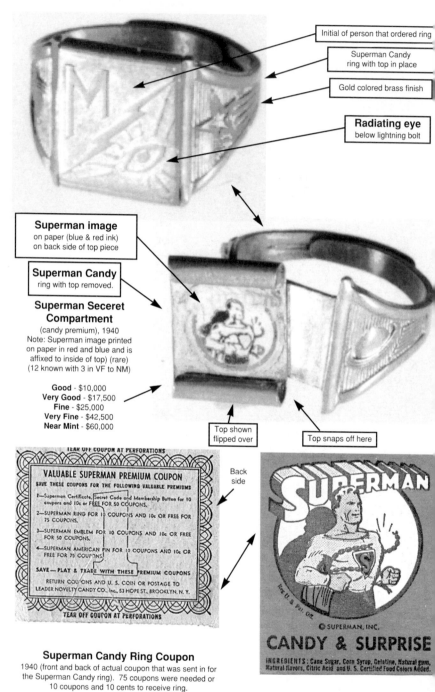

Initial of person that ordered ring

Superman Candy ring with top in place

Gold colored brass finish

Radiating eye
below lightning bolt

Superman image
on paper (blue & red ink)
on back side of top piece

Superman Candy
ring with top removed.

Superman Secret Compartment
(candy premium), 1940
Note: Superman image printed
on paper in red and blue and is
affixed to inside of top) (rare)
(12 known with 3 in VF to NM)

Good - $10,000
Very Good - $17,500
Fine - $25,000
Very Fine - $42,500
Near Mint - $60,000

Top shown flipped over

Top snaps off here

TEAR OFF COUPON AT PERFORATIONS

VALUABLE SUPERMAN PREMIUM COUPON
SAVE THESE COUPONS FOR THE FOLLOWING VALUABLE PREMIUMS

1—Superman Certificate, Secret Code and Membership Button for 10 coupons and 10c or FREE FOR 50 COUPONS.

2—SUPERMAN RING FOR 10 COUPONS AND 10c OR FREE FOR 75 COUPONS.

3—SUPERMAN EMBLEM FOR 10 COUPONS AND 10c OR FREE FOR 50 COUPONS.

4—SUPERMAN AMERICAN PIN FOR 10 COUPONS AND 10c OR FREE FOR 75 COUPONS.

SAVE — PLAY & TRADE WITH THESE PREMIUM COUPONS

RETURN COUPONS AND U. S. COIN OR POSTAGE TO
LEADER NOVELTY CANDY CO., Inc. 53 HOPE ST., BROOKLYN, N. Y.

TEAR OFF COUPON AT PERFORATIONS

Back side

SUPERMAN

CANDY & SURPRISE
INGREDIENTS: Cane Sugar, Corn Syrup, Gelatine, Natural gum, Natural flavors, Citric Acid and U. S. Certified Food Colors Added.

© SUPERMAN, INC.

Front side

Superman Candy Ring Coupon
1940 (front and back of actual coupon that was sent in for
the Superman Candy ring). 75 coupons were needed or
10 coupons and 10 cents to receive ring.
$25-$50

Note: Superman breaking chains logo was copied from coupon and placed on top of gum ring

Superman Gum Wrapper
1940 (rare)(in color)(5 coupons and 10 cents was required to receive the gum ring)
$750 - $1000

See next page for gum ring

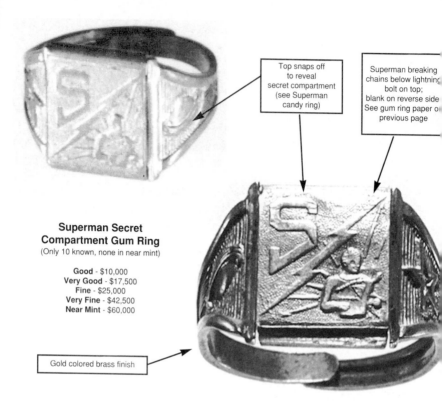

Top snaps off to reveal secret compartment (see Superman candy ring)

Superman breaking chains below lightning bolt on top; blank on reverse side See gum ring paper on previous page

Superman Secret Compartment Gum Ring
(Only 10 known, none in near mint)

Good - $10,000
Very Good - $17,500
Fine - $25,000
Very Fine - $42,500
Near Mint - $60,000

Gold colored brass finish

Superman Secret Compartment Gum Ring
(gum premium), 1940s, (rare)

Superman Tim (silver color)
(Given away at Superman Tim clothing stores)
1940s (scarce)(only one known in NM,
most examples exist in low grades)
(Recent sale, $10,000 cash plus $15,000
trade for only know near mint example)

Superman Tim Ring
Good - $3000
Very Good - $5,250
Fine - $7,500
Very Fine - $12,750
Near Mint - $18,000

Swastika
1940s (metal)
$30-$60

Squirrel

↑ **Sword In The Stone**
1960s (8 diff.)
$10-$20 ea.

Sylvester
1990s (metal)
$5-$10

Sweeney (see King Features)

Target Comics Ring
1940s (sterling silver)
$100-$200

Note: Also known as a Chinese **Good Luck Ring**, sold through Johnson Smith & Co. Catalogues in 1929. Symbols on ring stand for health, happiness, prosperiiy & prolonged life.

Sword in the Stone
(see Sleeping Beauty)
(soft plastic) (3 diff.)
1960s
$15-$25

Free Prizes for You

Target Comics

. . . wants you for a regular reader—so we are going to do something for you that no other comic magazine has done before—we are going to give you Free Prizes just for reading TARGET COMICS.

On this page are six prizes you can get absolutely free. For a complete list of Prizes just send a letter or a penny postal card to TARGET COMICS, 525 West 52nd Street, New York City, and say, "Please send me your Target Comics Prize List." Do this today!

Here's How You Get Your Prizes →

In each issue of TARGET COMICS there will appear a coupon similar to the one on this page. Clip these coupons and save them. The Prize List will tell you how many of these coupons you will need for each prize.

Double Value Target Comics Coupon

The coupon on this page has DOUBLE VALUE — in other words, it is worth twice as much as the ones which will appear in the future issues of TARGET COMICS. Save this coupon — DO NOT MAIL THE COUPON WHEN YOU SEND FOR YOUR PRIZE LIST.

This offer is void in any state or municipality where the redemption of coupons is prohibited, taxed, or restricted.

Win prizes by reading every issue of TARGET COMICS.

DOUBLE VALUE TARGET PRIZE COUPON

This coupon, clipped from the first issue of TARGET COMICS, will be redeemed at double the value of coupons appearing in future issues.
Write for your Prize List to TARGET COMICS, 525 West 52nd Street.

Fish

Sir Ector

Target Ring ad from Target Comics #1, Feb, 1940

Tarzan
1930s (metal) (rare)
$200-$400

Tarzan Flicker (1)
Tarzan swinging on vine to
Tarzan punching out a native
$20-$40 ea.

Tarzan Flicker (4)
Tarzan squaring off with a gorilla
to Tarzan having gorilla in a
headlock.
$20-$40 ea.

Tarzan Flicker (2)
Tarzan looking over his shoulder
at spear throwing natives to
Tarzan captured by two black
natives
$20-$40 ea.

Tarzan Flicker Paper
1960s (vending machine
(in color)
$15-$25

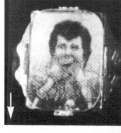

Tarzan Flicker
"Tazan" face to full figure shooting
bow & arrow. (red letters)
$15-$25

Tarzan Flicker (3)
Tarzan lifting a boulder in front of
a waterfall to Tarzan punching
another guy.
$20-$40 ea.

Tarzan Flicker (5)
Tarzan yelling to Tarzan caught
in vines.
$20-$40 ea.

Tarzan Flicker (6)
Tarzan landing from a vine to
Tarzan approching a black natve
whose back is to us.
$20-$40 ea.

↑ **Tarzan Flicker**
(silver) (plastic)
1960s
$15-$30 ea.

Tarzan Flicker (3)

↓

Tarzan Flicker (6)

↑ **Tarzan Flicker**
(blue plastic base)
1960s
$10-$20 ea.

↓ **Tarzan Flicker (1)**

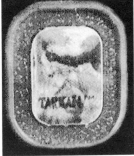

Tarzan Flicker (4)

↓

Bat swings to
hit baseball

↓ **Tarzan Flicker (2)**

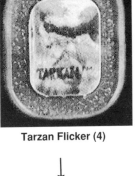

↓ **Tarzan Flicker (5)**

Ted Williams
Baseball, 1940s
$400-$900

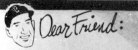

Here's my new NABISCO Shredded Wheat "Baseball Action Ring" which I hope you will enjoy.

By following these simple suggestions you can keep it in good condition for a long time: Adjust it to the exact size of your finger. Always keep it out of water and take it off when playing games.

I am sure some of your friends will want a ring like yours and I am therefore attaching a coupon which they can use.

Good luck to you!

Ted Williams

BOYS and GIRLS NOTICE!

I want you to have the most possible fun with my NABISCO SHREDDED WHEAT "Baseball Action Ring." Here are a few simple suggestions:

1. Remember it is a precision instrument. Treat it carefully and it will perform for you indefinitely.

2. I am a "southpaw" which means that I hit the ball left-handed. The small arrow on the white plastic base shows you the direction in which to flip the lever.

3. The wire supporting the baseball is part of the mainspring. If it should slip out of the tiny notch at the front of the ring, you can replace it in a jiffy.

Yours for a better batting average with NABISCO SHREDDED WHEAT.

Ted Williams

Send your name and address with 1 NABISCO Shredded Wheat Box top and 15¢ in coin (not stamps) to

NABISCO, DEPARTMENT "D".
BOX 372, NEW YORK 8, N.Y.
PLEASE PRINT CLEARLY!

NAME ....

ADDRESS ....

CITY .... STATE ......

Offer good in U. S. A. only.

**Ted Williams Coupon
& Paper**
1940s (scarce)
complete $100-$150

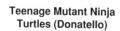

**Teenage Mutant Ninja
Turtles (Donatello)**

**Teenage Mutant Ninja
Turtles (Michael)**

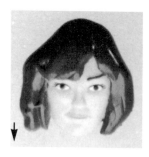

**Teenage Mutant Ninja
Turtles (April O'Nell)**

**Teenage Mutant Ninja
Turtles (Leonardo)**

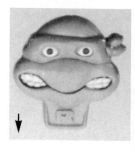

**Teenage Mutant Ninja
Turtles (Raphael)**

Teenage Mutant Ninja Turtles (Rock Steady)

Teenage Mutant Ninja Turtles (Splinter)

Teenage Mutant Ninja Turtles (Shredder)

Tekno Comix Logo
1994 (metal)(secret compartment)
$5

Teenage Mutant Ninja Turtles
1990s (8 diff.)(plastic in color)
Turtles - $30-$60 ea.
Others - $25-$50 ea.

Tennessee Jed Look-Around
1940s (metal)(rare in VF-NM)
$150-$450

Terry & the Pirates Gold Detector Ring Ad Paper
1940s, $5-$10

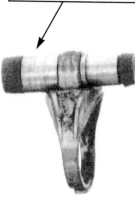

Secret chamber hides deposit of **REAL GOLD** magnified by special microscope lens.

Terry & the Pirates
1950s (plastic)(Cracker Jacks)
$25-$50

Three Stooges Flic
(Larry)

Three Stooges Flick
(Moe)

Three Stooges Flick
(3 diff.) 1959
$10-$20 ea.

Terry & the Pirates
Gold Detector
1940s
$75-$150

Three Stooges Flicker
(Curley)

The 3 Stooges Flicker Paper
1960s (vending machine paper)(in color)
$15-$30

Thunderbird
1930s (rare) (see Lone Wolf)
$200-$400

Tiger Eye
(4 diff.) (blue, green, and red tops)
1960s
$25-$50 ea.

Thundercats Flicker
1986 (plastic secret compartment flicker
ring (Burger King premium)(top slides off to
reveal secret compartment)
$15-$30

Thundercats Flicker
(in package)(plastic secret comparrtment
ring)(Burger King premium)
(top slides off to reveal secret
compartment)1986
$30

Tillie The Toller
(see King Features & Post Tin)

Tim (see Superman
Tim)

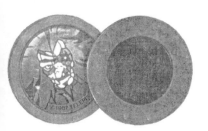

Thundercats Flicker
(villain) (red plastic with a sliding
cover that is transparent
red plastic that slides over image Telepix),
1987
$15-$30

Tim Ring
1930s (rare)(metal)
(sold at Tim Stores)
$300-$600

Timothy (Disney)
oval, 1950s
$50-$100

Tom Corbett Face
1950s (silver color metal)
$50

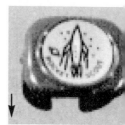

**Tom Corbett (3)
Rocket Scout**

Timothy (Disney)
square, 1950s
$50-$100

**Tom Corbett (1)
Girl Uniform**

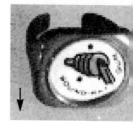

**Tom Corbett (4)
Sound-Ray Gun**

**Tom Corbett (5)
Space Academy**

Tinkerbelle
1970s (plastic)
$5-$10

Tom & Jerry Flicker
1970s (blue plastic base)
$10-$20

**Tom Corbett (2)
Parallo-Ray Gun**

**Tom Corbett (6)
Space Cadet
Dress Uniform**

Tom Corbett (7)
Space Cadet Insignia

Tom Corbett (11)
Strato Telescope

Tom Corbett Rocket
(metal), 1950s
$175-$350

Tom Corbett (8)
Space Cruiser

Tom Corbett (12)
Tom Corbet Space Cadet

Tom Corbett
(plastic) (12 diff.)(Kelloggs)
1952
$10-$20 ea.

Tom Mix Circus
1930s (see Billy
West & Cowboy
Riding Horse)
$50-$100

Tom Corbett (9)
Space Helmet

14 kt. white gold finish
metal ring

Tom Corbett (10)
Space Suit

Tom Mix Deputy
1935 (rare)(Tom Mix chewing
gum premium)(75 certificates needed to get ring (each attached to a
Tom Mix chewing gum wrapper)(scarce)
Good - $1375
Fine - $2750
Near Mint - $5500

FREE!!! FREE!!! FREE!!! FREE!!!
⭐ MIX DEPUTY RING

SAVE 75 TOM MIX CERTIFICATES AND GET A 14 KT.
white gold finished TOM MIX DEPUTY RING. - You then become a
TOM MIX DEPUTY. - A full fledged fearless champion of law and order.

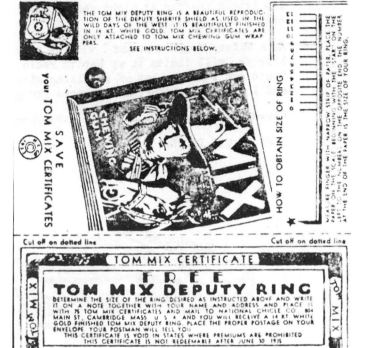

THE TOM MIX DEPUTY RING IS A BEAUTIFUL REPRODUC-
TION OF THE DEPUTY SHERIFF SHIELD AS USED IN THE
WILD DAYS OF THE WEST. IT IS BEAUTIFULLY FINISHED
IN 14 KT. WHITE GOLD. TOM MIX CERTIFICATES ARE
ONLY ATTACHED TO TOM MIX CHEWING GUM WRAP-
PERS.

SEE INSTRUCTIONS BELOW.

Cut off on dotted line   Cut off on dotted line

TOM MIX CERTIFICATE
FREE
TOM MIX DEPUTY RING

DETERMINE THE SIZE OF THE RING DESIRED AS INSTRUCTED ABOVE AND WRITE
IT ON A NOTE TOGETHER WITH YOUR NAME AND ADDRESS AND PLACE 75
TOM MIX CERTIFICATES AND MAIL TO NATIONAL CHICLE CO. 804
MAIN ST., CAMBRIDGE MASS. U.S.A. AND YOU WILL RECEIVE A 14 KT. WHITE
GOLD FINISHED TOM MIX DEPUTY RING. PLACE THE PROPER POSTAGE ON YOUR
ENVELOPE. YOUR POSTMAN WILL TELL YOU.
THIS CERTIFICATE IS VOID IN STATES WHERE PREMIUMS ARE PROHIBITED
THIS CERTIFICATE IS NOT REDEEMABLE AFTER JUNE 30 1935.

TOM MIX CERTIFICATE

ELEPHANT HAIR GOOD LUCK RING
Made with genuine elephant hair enclosed in gold plated band

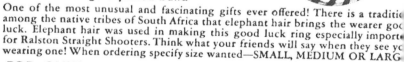

One of the most unusual and fascinating gifts ever offered! There is a tradition
among the native tribes of South Africa that elephant hair brings the wearer good
luck. Elephant hair was used in making this good luck ring especially imported
for Ralston Straight Shooters. Think what your friends will say when they see you
wearing one! When ordering specify size wanted—SMALL, MEDIUM OR LARGE.

FOR ONLY 1 RALSTON WHEAT CEREAL BLUE SEAL AND 10¢

Tom Mix Elephant Hair Good Luck
Ring (ad from comic book shown above), 1940s (rare)
Ring price - $100-$200

For Better Breakfasts
's RALSTON

ONE—Regular Hot Ralston, cooks in 5 minutes

TWO—Instant Hot Ralston, cooks in 10 seconds

THREE — ...... ston — the -eat cereal

'd packages

PRINTED IN U.S.A

Dear Straight Shooter:

Here is your Tom Mix "Look-Around" Ring from the Ralston Straight Shooters Radio Program.

We know you're going to have a lot of fun with it, and surprise your friends by being able to see around corners and over your shoulder . . . without turning your head!

Here's the way to use your "Look-Around" Ring. Put it on your *left* hand with the "crossed pistol" design toward the ends of your fingers. Now, the open peephole above the T-M Bar insignia will be toward your thumb. This is the part **you** look through—and you can see objects to the left and slightly in back of you.

Your "Look-Around" Ring is adjustable to fit any finger size. To make it smaller, squeeze the overlapping prongs together. To make it large, spread them apart.

Your Straight Shooter Pal,

Tom Mix Look-Around Paper
1940s, $60-$80

Tom Mix Look Around
1940s (metal)
$75-$150

SIGNET RING

A lucky Signet Ring just like Tom wears. 24-carat gold plated. *With your own initial* set in simulated gold over a special onyx black panel. Fits any finger. For one Ralston (hot cereal) box top and 10¢ or two box tops.

Tom Mix Lucky Initial Signet
1930s (24 kt. gold plated)
(customer had his own initial placed on top of ring)
$100-$200

Tom Mix Lucky Signet Paper
(complete) $60-$80

For Better Breakfasts
It's RALSTON

ONE—Regular Hot Ralston, cooks in 5 minutes

TWO—Instant Hot Ralston, cooks in 10 seconds

THREE—Shredded Ralston—the delicious bite size ready-to-eat cereal

Whole Grain Cereals in the Red-an[...]

C2475A—1-46

Diagonal mirror enables viewer to look around corners

Tom Mix Look-Around Pa[per]
1940s, $60-$80

Tom Mix Look-Around Ring
1940s (metal)(gold color finish)
$75-$150

TOM MIX MAGNET RING

Magnet in head of ring picks up pins, paper clips and other small metal objects!

Fits any finger. Just squeeze ring together here to make it smaller.

For Better Breakfasts ... It's
RALSTON

ONE—Instant Ralston, cooks in 10 seconds.
TWO—Regular Ralston, cooks in 5 minutes.
THREE—Shredded Ralston, the delicious *bite-size* ready-to-eat cereal.

Whole Grain Cereals in the Red-and-White Checkerboard Packages.

C2403A-9-48   Printed in U. S. A.

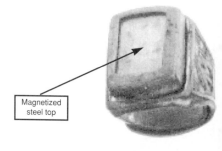

Magnetized steel top

Tom Mix Magnet Ring
1940s (metal)
$45-$90

Tom Mix Magnet Ring Paper
1940s, $20-$30

ANSWERS to TOM MIX mysteries

THE TELEVISION MURDER: Photograph of Mintmore (Frame 3) shows he needed thick glasses. Why didn't he have them on if he was watching Television when shot? Window glass shows bullet was fired from inside room. Hole is always smaller on side where bullet enters.

THE PHONE BOOTH MURDER: If man was talking on phone when shot, receiver would not be on hook. Bullet entered head on side that would have been toward back wall of booth.

THE SELF-DEFENSE MURDER: Bruises show mur-derer used own hands to fake marks on neck. If someone had choked him, the little-finger mark would have been at the bottom of the neck . . . not at top.

THE MATCH MURDER: Matches torn from left side of match book shows left-handed man. Watch on right wrist of one suspect shows he is left-handed.

THE MURDERED TRAPPER: If cabin was 50° below, man couldn't have written suicide note with pen. Ink would have frozen instantly.

Blowing through top of ring creates whirring sound

spinner missing

Tom Mix Musical Ring
1940s (metal)(also see Jack Armstrong Egyptian Whistle ring) complete $50-$100

Tom Mix Musical Ring Paper
1940s, $60-$80

Slide base in & out while blowing through whistle

Engraving over sterling silver top

Tom Mix Nail
1930s (same form as Gene Autry Nail) $20-$40

Tom Mix Signature
(sterling top), 1940s $100-$200

Tom Mix Sliding Whistle
1940s (metal) $50-$100

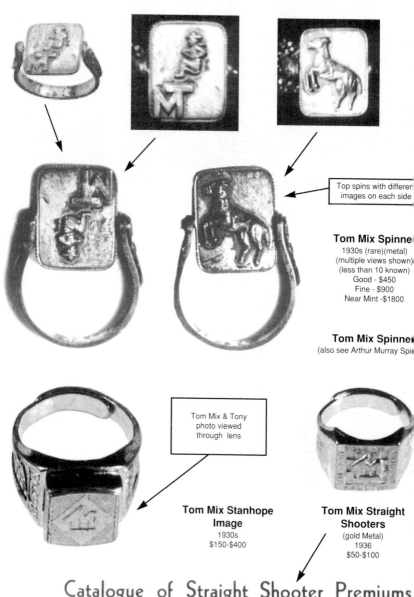

Top spins with different
images on each side

Tom Mix Spinner
1930s (rare)(metal)
(multiple views shown)
(less than 10 known)
Good - $450
Fine - $900
Near Mint -$1800

Tom Mix Spinner
(also see Arthur Murray Spinner)

Tom Mix & Tony
photo viewed
through lens

**Tom Mix Stanhope
Image**
1930s
$150-$400

**Tom Mix Straight
Shooters**
(gold Metal)
1936
$50-$100

Catalogue of Straight Shooter Premiums

STRAIGHT SHOOTER RING

This ring is a beauty. Every Straight Shooter should own one.
Has Tom Mix' TM Bar Brand in raised letters on top and a
six shooter and steer's head on the sides. Glitters like gold!
Fits any finger.   FREE for only 1 Ralston Box Top.

Tom Mix Straight Shooter Ring paper
from catalogue. Catalogue value $75-$100

Tom Mix Target
1930s (metal)(Marlin Guns)
$100-$250

Tom Mix Straight Shooter paper
1936, $60-$80 (complete)

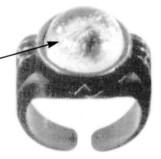

Cat's eye
glows in dark

Tom Mix Tiger Eye
1950s (plastic)
$125-$275

Tom Mix Tiger-Eye Paper
$75-$100

Tonka Jewel
1990s
$5-$10

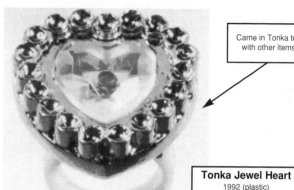

Came in Tonka to
with other items

Tonka Jewel Heart
1992 (plastic)
$5-$10

Toots (see Post Tin)

Tonto Plastic
Photo, 1940s (Also see Lone
Ranger Plastic)
$30-$60

Troll Doll
1960s
$15-$25

Tonto Picture
1938 (plastic), ice cream comic book
giveaway (rare)(also see Lone Ranger
Picture)(less than 10 known)
Good - $625
Fine - $1250
Near Mint - $2500

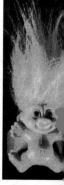

Troll Doll
1992 (5diff.) (each doll has var. hair colors)
$1-$2 ea.

Troll Rings (on card, 1992) $6 w/card

Tweety Bird
1980s (metal)
$5-$10

Tweety Bird
1980s (metal)(small)
$10-$20

Troll Rings (on crd, 1992)
$6 w/card (rings diff. than previous page)

Tweety Bird
1980s (metal)
$5-$10

Twinkie Shoe
1940s (metal)
$75-$150

Twinkie The Kid
1970s (snack cake)
$4-$8

Twist Flicker
1960s (plastic)
$5-$10

LET'S TWIST
FLICKER RING

Twist Flicker paper
1960s (rare)(in color)
$15-$25

Uncle Creepy
1970s, (Warren) (metal)
(also see Cousin Eerie)
$100-$200

Twist Flicker
1960s "Twist" girl in skirt with
green top dancing in front. Two
smaller figures dancing in background.
$5-$10

U.N.C.L.E. Flicker
(see Man From --)

Ultraman Small Face
1980s (metal)
$50-$100

Ultraman Cartoon
1980s (metal, in color)
$15-$25

Underdog
1970s (metal cloisonne)
$100-$150

Ultraman Figure
1980s (metal)
$15-$30

Underdog
1970s (plastic)(silver over red)
$150-$275

Ultraman Large Face
1980s (metal)
$40-$75

Underdog
1970s (plastic)(black over yellow)
$125-$200

Universal Monster Flicker (The Creature)
(both images shown)

Universal Monster Flicker Paper
1960s (vending machine paper)(rare)(in color)
$20-$35

Universal Monster Flicker (Mummy)
(both images shown)

Universal Monster Flicker (Dracula)
(both images shown)

Universal Monster Flicker
1960s (original silver base)(scarce)
(set of 6)(the 2 Casper flickers may be part of set)
$40-$70 ea.

Dracula

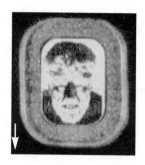

Wolfman

↑ **Universal Monster Flicker**
(plastic)(blue base)
1960s (scarce)
$30-$50 ea.

Universal Monsters Flick
1960s (monster/Warewolf)
$20-$35

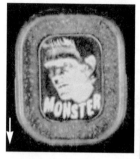

Monster

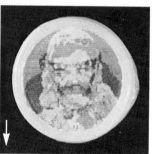

Universal Monster Flicker
1960s (Creature/Wolfman)
$20-$35

Universal Monster Flicke
1960s (Mummy/Wolfman)
$20-$35

Mummy

Phantom

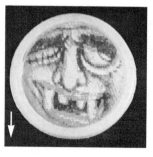

Universal Monster Flicker
1960s (Hunchback of Notre Dame)
$20-$35

Universal Monster Flick
1960s (Phantom of the
Opera/Wolfman)
$20-$35

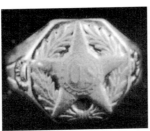

U.S. Marshal
1930s (rare)(metal)
$300-$600

USN Gumball
1940s (gumball)(metal)
$5-$10

USA Astronaut Flicker
1960s (in color)
$5-$10

USN Store Card
1950s (3 variations)
$10-$20 ea.

USA/KKK Ring
(100%)1930s
(flips to reveal KKK)
(radio) (rare)(metal)
$400-$1000

Valentine Flicker
(see Cupid & Heart-Arrow
flicker), 1960s (plastic)
$5-$10

CUPID FLICKER RING

U.S. Keds (metal)
(see Kolonel Keds)
1960s
$55-$110

Valentine Flicker Paper
1960s, (Cupid Flicker)(vending
machine)(in color), $8-$15

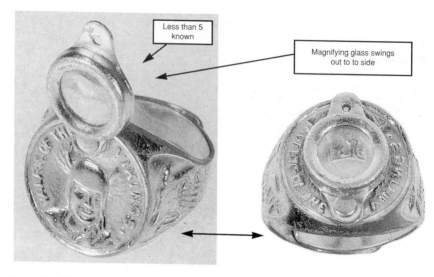

Less than 5 known

Magnifying glass swings out to to side

Valric The Viking Magnifying
1940s (All Rye Flakes premium)
(very rare)(also see ROA Magnifying)
Good - $1750
Very Good - $2625
Fine - $3500
Very Fine - $5250
Near Mint - $7000

Victor Mature
(See Movie Star Photo)

Victory Ring
1940s, $5-$10

Volcano (see Quake...)

Walnettos Initial Saddle
1940s (metal)
$30-$60

Wacky Races-Mutley
1970s (metal)
$10-$20

Wanda Hendrix
Photo, 1950s
$10-$20

Watch Flicker
1960s (Face of
Elgin watch with
hands flickening
around)
$5-$10 ea.

Weapon, Gun
1960s (red over silver)
$20-$35

Weapon, Knife
1960s (blue over silver)
(also see Sleeping Beauty)
$20-$35

Weather Bird
1950s
(shoes)
$75-$150

Western Flicker
1960s (plastic, circular)
(green plastic bases)(set of 5)
(al lcame wrapped in clear plastic)
$10-$20 ea.

Wheat Chex Decoder
1940s (paper)
$30-$60

Wheaties
(see Compass)

Whistle Bomb (also see
Lone Ranger Atomic Bomb)

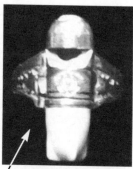

White
plastic
end

Metal whistle
front

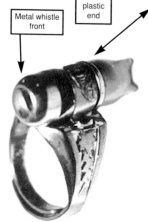

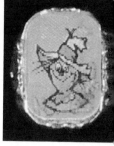

**Wizard of Oz Flicker
(Scarcrow)**
1967 (plastic)(shows both images)
$15-$25

Whistle Bomb
(glow-in-dark),, 1940s (rare)(metal)
GD - $300, FN - $600, NM - $1200

Witchiepoo (see H.R. Puff n' Stuff)

Wimpy
1960s (silver color metal)(in color)
(also see Popeye)
$75 - $150

Wile E. Coyote (see Looney Tunes)

Winnie Winkle (see Post Tin)

**Wizard of Oz Flicker
(Dorothy)**
1967 (plastic)(shows both images)
$15-$25

**Wizard of Oz Flicker
(Tin Man)**
1967 (plastic)(shows
both images)
$15-$25

Wizard of Oz Flicker (Witch)
1967 (plastic)
$15-$25

Wizard of Oz Flicker (Wizard)
1967 "Off to See The Wizard" with picture of OZ
in background to full cartoon figure of cowardly
lion
$15-$25

Wizard of Oz Flicker
1967 (plastic)(set of 12)
(priced above)

Wizard of Oz Flicker
1970s (green base, green flicker)
$10-$20

Wizard of Oz Flicker
1970s (blue base, green flicker)
$10-$20

William Boyd
(Hopalong Cassidy, see Real Photos)

Winnie Winkle
(see Post Tin)

Wolfman (see Universal Monsters

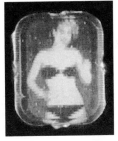

Woman Dancer Flicker
1950s (thick top)
$10-$20

Wonder Bread
(plastic), 1960s
$5-$10

Wonder Woman
Logo, 1980s (metal)
$35-$70

Wonder Woman
Logo, 1980s (metal)
$35-$70

Wonder Woman
logo, 1980s (metal)
$35-$70

Woodstock
1980s (metal)
$10-$20

Woody Woodpecker
1992 (metal)
$2-$4

Woody Woodpecker
1970s (plastic)
$5-$10

Woodstock
1980s (metal cloisonne)
$10-$20

Woody Woodpecker
1970s (plastic)
$5-$10

Woody Woodpecker
1980s (metal cloisonne)
$10-$25

Woody Woodpecker Stamp
Club, 1960s (2 diff. colors)(Kelloggs Rice
Krispies cereal premium)
$100-$200

World's Fair
1933 Chicago
$15-$50

World's Fair
1933 Chicago
$15-$50

World's Fair
1933 Chicago
$15-$50

World's Fair
1933 Chicago(silver/blue top)
$15-$50

World's Fair
1933 Chicago
(Indian head) (bronze)
$15-$40

World's Fair
1834 Chicago
$15-$40

World's Fair
1939 (plastic top)
$15-$40

World's Fair
1934 Chicago
(Indian head)
(pewter), $15-$40

World's Fair
1934 Hall of Science15-$40

World's Fair
1939 (plastic)
(white, blue, green, orange tops;
silver, gold metal base versions)
$60-$120 ea.

World's Fair
1934 Chicago
$15-$40

World's Fair
1939 (silver metal)
$15-$40

World's Fair Flicker
1964 (plastic)
$5-$10

World's Fair
1934 Chicago
$15-$40

World Fair
1939 (metal, blue)
$15-$40

World's Fair Flicker
"Souvenir of the New York Worlds
Fair 1964-1965" to picture of the
globe sculpture
$5-$10

KIDS!

Wyatt Earp
MARSHAL'S RING!

⭐ **Gleaming Sterling Silver!**
⭐ **Fits Any Finger!**
⭐ **Looks Like a Real Marshal's Badge!**

WITH YOUR INITAL

ONLY **25¢** AND 2 CHEERIOS BOXTOPS

A12000

Printed in U.S.A.

Wyatt Earp Marshal
1950s (metal)(Cheerios)
$40-$80

X-Men Gold
1993 (Diamond Comics Distr.)
(w/diamond chip, 25 made)
$850

Wyatt Earp Paper
$35-$50

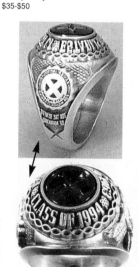

X-O
(Valiant Comics)
1993
$60-$80

X-Men Silver
1993 (Diamond Comics Distr.)
$150

X-Men Xavier Institute Class Ring
1994 (excellent detail)
Gold (10K, 250 made) - $400
Sterling (2,500 made) - $75
Bronze finished pewter (unlimited) - $2

OFFICIAL RING

© WALT DISNEY PRODUCTIONS

Infringements will be prosecuted
All Rights Protected

Zorro (Z)
1960s (plastic)(vending machine)
$35-$70

Zorro Ring Paper
1960s (vending machine
paper)(scarce)
$20-$35

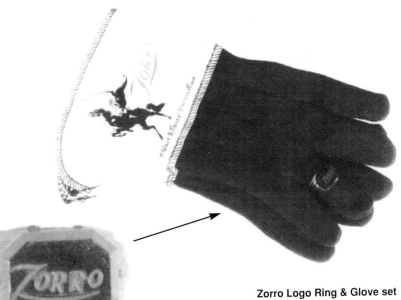

Zorro Logo Ring
1960s (vending machine)
(silver & black base versions)
$40-$80

Zorro Logo Ring & Glove set
1960s (ring sold with Zorro
glove)(silver base version)
$75-$150

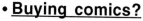

Howdy Doody Raised Face
1950s, $150

Humpty Dumpty
1970s, $10

Howdy Doody TV Flicker
1950s, $600

Indian, Goudy Gum
1940s, $150

H.R. Pufnstuf
1970s (7 diff.), $40

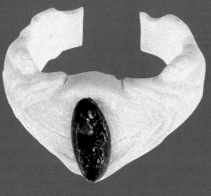

Jack Armstrong Dragon's Eye
1940s (glows in dark), $1000

Jack Armstrong Egyptian Whistle
1940s, $125

Knights Of Columbus
1940s, $3000

King Features, Sweeney
1950s, $40

Lassie Friendship
1950s, $180

King Kong
1962, $10

Laugh-in Flicker
1968 (set of 16), $20

Lone Ranger Atom Bomb
1946 (watch atoms smash inside tail fin)
$100

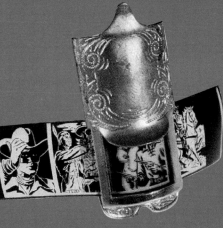

Lone Ranger Photo Test
1940s, $1800

Lone Ranger Saddle Film
1950, $200 complete

Lone Ranger Gold Ore
1940s, $4700

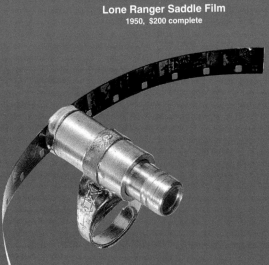

Lone Ranger Movie Film
1949, $150 complete

Mack
1940s, $75

McDonalds Heart
1970s, $20

Martian Fink
1950s, $20

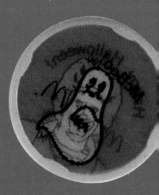

McDonalds McBoo Flicker
1970s, $15

Marvel Flicker
1970s (set of 12), $20

Mickey Mouse Glass Dome
1930s, $500

Mister Softee
1950s, $50

Mystic Horror Rings vending machine paper
1950s, $25

Monkees Flicker
1966 (set of 12), $60 ea.

Pac Man
1980s, $25

Mork & Mindy Flicker
1979, $35

Pinocchio Figure
1960s, $80

Poll Parrot Face
1950s, $40

Radio Orphan Annie Altascope
1940s, $25,000

Popeye Flicker
1960s (blue base), $20

Radio Orphan Annie Initial
1940s, $4500

Quisp Space Disk Whistle
1960s, $350

Radio Orphan Annie Magnifying
1940s, $4200

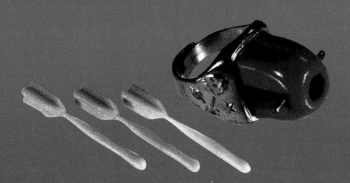

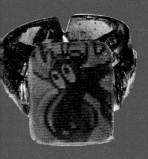

**Rocket to the Moon
(one of two released from
the Kellogg's library)**
1951, $1200 complete

**Rocky & Bullwinkle
Flicker (Bullwinkle)**
1961, $50

**Rocky & Bullwinkle vending
machine paper**
1961, $35

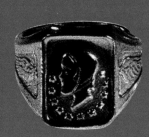

Rosalie Gimple
1940s, $250

Shadow Blue Coal
1941 (glows in dark), $550

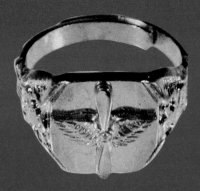

Sky Bird
1940s, $150

Spider
1930s, $10,000

**Snap, Crackle, Pop
(Crackle)**
1950s, $300

Spider-Man Vitamin
1960s, $100

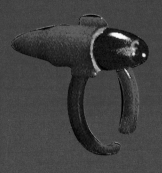

Space Patrol Cosmic Glow
1950s, $800

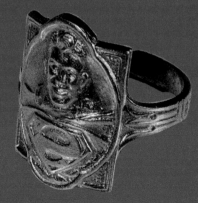

Superman Crusader
1940s, $250

Superman Pep Airplane
1940s (mounted, ready to shoot), $250

Superman Secret Compartment
(candy)
1940, $70,000

uperman vending machine flicker paper
1960s, $125

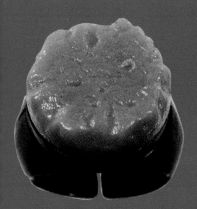

Superman Kryptonite
1990, $30

Superman Secret Compartment
(gum)
1940s, $70,000

Superman Prize
1940, $120,000

**Teenage Mutant Ninja
Turtles (Raphael)**
1990s (set of 8), $60

Tarzan Flicker
1960s, $40

Tom Corbett Face
1950s, $50

**Tarzan Flicker Ring vending
machine paper**
1960s, $25

Universal Monster Flicker
1960s (original silver base), $70

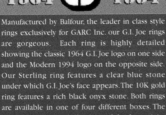

THE
OVERSTREET
PREMIUM RING
PRICE GUIDE

Other Publications From Overstreet:

THE OVERSTREET COMIC BOOK PRICE GUIDE
by Robert M. Overstreet

THE OVERSTREET COMIC BOOK GRADING GUIDE
by Robert M. Overstreet & Gary M. Carter

THE OVERSTREET COMIC BOOK MONTHLY

THE OVERSTREET GOLD & SILVER QUARTERLY

THE OVERSTREET COMICS & CARDS PRICE GUIDE

**THE OVERSTREET INDIAN ARROWHEADS
IDENTIFICATION AND PRICE GUIDE**
by Robert M. Overstreet

THE
OVERSTREET
PREMIUM RING
PRICE GUIDE

FIRST
EDITION

ROBERT M. OVERSTREET

SPECIAL ADVISORS
Bill Campbell, Steve Geppi, Ted Hake, Robert Hall, Mike Herz,
Bob Hritz, Roger Hutchinson, Harry Matetsky, Kevin Pipes, Mike Renegar,
Bruce Rosen, John Snyder, Howard C. Weinberger,

THE OVERSTREET PREMIUM RING PRICE GUIDE (1st Edition) is an original publication by Robert M. Overstreet.

Distributed to the book trade by
Antique Trader Books
100 Bryant Street
P.O. Box 1050
Dubuque, IA 52004
Phone: 1-800-334-7165
Fax: 1-800-583-0880

ACKNOWLEDGMENTS

he publication of this premiere edition was made possible by the early inspiration of "Little" Jimmy Dempsey and the constant encouragement and advice of John Snyder, Bruce Rosen, Steve Geppi, Harry Matetsky, Mike Herz, and Bob Hritz. These enthusiastic hobbyists gave freely of their time and knowledge to make this book the most comprehensive and informative work on premium rings published.

Special recognition is also due Gary Guzzo for his management and marketing advice and to Bonnie Berryman for her advance information on Marvel Comics' ring program and also for supplying rings for photographing; and to Denise Treko for furnishing information about the Tekno Comix ring program and cheerfully supplying photos.

I would also like to thank Howard C. Weinberger for his excellent article on flicker rings as well as his invaluable contribution of data and information about flicker rings; and Howard's photographer, Jeff Kermath, who spent hours photographing rings for this edition.

A very special thanks is also due Bruce Rosen who supplied hundreds of rings for photographing as well as for his expert guidance in the layout, execution, and arrangement of detail for this edition; to Dave Eskenazi who supplied rings for photographing; to John Barry of Planet Studios for supplying photographs; to Bob Barrett for sending photographs; and to Danny Fuchs for his contribution of advice and material for illustration.

Other contributors to this edition include Dave Anderson, Ron Breidenbach, Paul Burke, Bill Campbell, Paul Deion, Dave Eskenazi, Robert Hall, Bill Hughes, Steve Ison, R.C. Lettner, Jennifer Menken, Rex Miller, Kevin Pipes, Ed Pragler, Scott Rona, Joseph Sain, Art Thomas, Denise Treko, Evelyn Wilson, who all have my sincere thanks.

Thanks is also due Mike Renegar, Tony Overstreet, Todd Hoffer, and Gary M. Carter for their help in scanning, layout, and design of this edition; David Noah for his help with proofing; and to my wife Carol Overstreet for her valuable advice concerning layout, editorial, and color design.

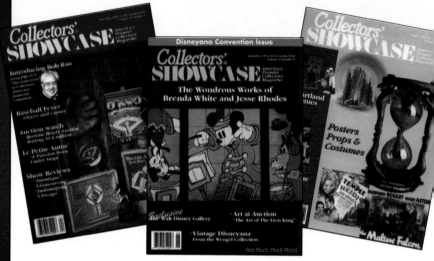

TABLE OF CONTENTS

FOREWORD

By Bob Hritz

Threlling of the tower bell" and "drone of a plane"; the magic word "Shazam," a clap of thunder and bolt of lightning; "who knows what evil lurks in the hearts of men?": These opening phrases of yesteryear's heroes left an indelible mark on the minds of countless children.

Thousands of Americans were entertained by their favorite heroes from radio programs, pulps, comic books, movies, and serials. Needless to say, the producers and sponsors were aware of America's love affair with these imaginary heroes. In fact, they were very interested in keeping the fans loyal to the character and more particularly to the <u>product.</u> And what better way than to provide a simple device to guarantee this –The Ring! A small item that could be worn was certainly the most astonishingly clever marketing device ever created. The ring provided the sponsor with the product demographics it needed. Not only did they learn who was buying their product, but from what areas, age group, sex, etc. This important information was used in targeting future markets for product sales.

> Sponsors used the premium ring as a clever marketing tool to encourage kids to try their products.

Today, it costs companies millions to collect the same information. Being the first kid on the block to display this new treasure was undoubtedly this week's claim to fame. "How do I get one?" was repeated over and over and the marketing hook was taken. An advertising genius never had the power of persuasion that any child possesses. We raced to the corner to get a copy of that special comic, urged mom and dad to use only "clean burning Blue Coal" in the furnace, nagged for more boxes of Instant Ralston, and argued the health value of "nutritious, delicious, Ovaltine." How else could a sponsor place a sales representative in every home? Not only were boys and girls sales reps, but they also learned the value of work. It took all day to mow a lawn with the push mower to earn fifty cents to send for a Blue Coal Shadow glow-in-the-dark ring and a Green Hornet secret compartment seal ring.

This reference work has been many years in the making and is the result of long hours of extensive research, photographic work, and invaluable consultation with ring collectors, historians, and dealers across the country. This book has hundreds of new ring listings and detailed information never published before. Many new rings and sets of rings have been recently discovered, as well as amazing record prices paid for certain rare rings; all of which are reflected in this landmark first edition.

As you make your way through this phenomenal volume, you will note that most radio, TV, movie, and comic character stars (and/or their mythos) have been immortalized with some kind of premium ring. The premiums were usually offered by sponsors, publicity departments, and publishers in an attempt to create a desire in consumers (mostly children) for the program, film, or comic. This marketing strategy is apparently so successful that it is still being utilized to this very day.

> These treasures of childhood were placed carefully in our special boxes, bags and drawers to avoid having mom or dad throw them away!

We can look back on these rings with more than fondness. If you doubt this, how can you explain their survival? These treasures of childhood were placed carefully in our special boxes, bags and drawers to avoid the ultimate demise of premiums–mom throwing them away. They survived teen years, dating, and even raising our own families. Today, the collector awaits the mail anxiously for his newest rings purchased from fellow collectors. The thrill rivals that of his childhood. Going through a portfolio of investments never brought forth the flashes of excitement and wonderful memories that handling one of these rings can. Today's ring collector pursues his hobby with no less zeal than when he first wanted one way back then. And he's not alone.

Introduction

Many rings are offered each year to attract new collectors in this market. For instance, DC recently produced the Superman magnet and Green Lantern squirt rings. Matchbox developed a beautiful set of 68 rings called the "Ring Raiders," and Mattel produced a popular series called "Polly Pockets" with its own styled ring box. Marvel has also released its new X-Men series. Many cereal boxes are adorned with offers of rings. Lucky Charms displayed the Lucky Horseshoe ring and King Vitamin also got into the act with the Hologram ring. Kelloggs Sugar Corn Pops offered a set of 28 football insignia rings–a classic set of metal beauties. Disney offered a set of five different stamp rings featuring Minnie Mouse in 1991. Thousands of collectors are eagerly waiting each year for new offerings to add to their collections.

Ring prices are always changing as the market continues to grow. The wise investor should keep up with the latest sales and discoveries, using this book only as a guide.

The increased interest in this market has prompted the author to develop the following reference and price report. We hope it will provide up-to-date information in this new and exciting part of collecting comic related memorabilia. A special thanks to all who helped in the compilation of this unique listing of these wonderful little toys–the rings!

GRADE AND ITS RELATION TO VALUE

CONDITION IS THE KEY TO VALUE - Condition plays a large role in determining value for most rings. As one might imagine, the more expensive the ring, the more important condition and accurate grading become. The value of a ring in Mint condition can be as much as 10 times that of the same ring in just Good condition. For a ring to bring the highest value, it must be complete, original, unrestored and in top condition.

100 MOST VALUABLE PREMIUM RINGS

VALUE	RANK	RING TYPE
$125,000	1	Superman Of America (prize)(comic books)
$60,000	2	Superman Secret Compartment (candy)
$60,000	2	Superman Secret Compartment (gum)
$25,000	4	Radio Orphan Annie Altascope
$20,000	5	Operator Five
$18,000	6	Superman Tim
$10,000	7	Spider
$9,000	8	Sky King Kaleidoscope
$7,500	9	Cisco Kid Secret Compartment
$7,000	10	Valric The Viking

VALUE	RANK	RING TYPE
$5,500	11	Tom Mix Deputy
$5,200	12	Howdy Doody Jack in the Box
$4,800	13	Radio Orphan Annie Initial
$4,700	14	Lone Ranger Gold Ore
$4,500	15	Frank Buck Black Leopard (W. Fair)
$4,500	15	Radio Orphan Annie Magnifying
$3,500	17	Lone Ranger (ice cream)
$3,000	18	Buck Rogers Repeller Ray
$3,000	18	Knights of Columbus
$3,000	18	Buck Rogers Sylvania Bulb

VALUE	RANK	RING TYPE
$3,000	21	Spiderman (gold)
$2,800	22	Frank Buck Black Leopard (bronze)
$2,500	23	Captain Marvel
$2,500	23	Tonto (ice cream)
$2,500	23	Joe Louis Face
$2,200	26	Green Hornet (plastic)

VALUE	RANK	RING TYPE
$2,100	27	Captain Midnight Mystic Sun God
$2,000	28	Batman Bat Signal (gold)
$1,800	29	Lone Ranger Photo (test)
$1,800	29	Frank Buck Black Leopard (silver)

VALUE	RANK	RING TYPE
$1,800	29	Tom Mix Spinner
$1,600	32	Quisp Figural
$1,600	32	Dick Tracy Monogram
$1,500	34	Captain Hawks/Melvin Purvis Scarab
$1,500	34	Clarabelle Face/Hat
$1,200	36	Captain Video Flying Saucer (complete)
$1,200	36	Green Hornet Secret Compartment
$1,200	36	Don Winslow Member
$1,200	36	Whistle Bomb
$1,200	36	Radio Orphan Annie Triple Mystery

VALUE	RANK	RING TYPE
$1,200	36	Rocket To The Moon (complete)
$1,000	42	Barnabas Collins (Dark Shadows)
$1,000	42	Captain Midnight Signet (1957)
$1,000	42	Captain Video Pendant
$1,000	42	Jack Armstrong Dragon's Eye
$1,000	42	Joe Louis Figural
$1,000	42	Major Mars Rocket (complete)
$1,000	42	Shadow Carey Salt
$1,000	42	Spawn (gold)
$1,000	42	U.S.A. (KKK)

VALUE	RANK	RING TYPE
$900	51	Sky King Aztec Emerald Calendar
$900	51	Ted Williams Baseball
$850	53	Buck Rogers Ring of Saturn
$850	53	X-Men (gold)
$800	55	Roy Rogers Hat
$800	55	Space Patrol Cosmic Glow
$750	57	Archie (gold)
$750	57	Lone Ranger Secret Compartment-Airforce
$750	57	Lone Ranger Secret Compartment-Army
$750	57	Lone Ranger Secret Compartment-Marines

VALUE	RANK	RING TYPE
$750	57	Lone Ranger Secret Compartment-Navy
$750	57	Rin Tin Tin (complete)

VALUE	RANK	RING TYPE
$750	57	Shadow (gold)
$700	64	Sky King Mystery Picture
$625	65	Jack Armstrong Baseball Centennial
$600	66	Bullet Pen
$600	66	Captain Video Secret Seal (copper top)
$600	66	Cisco Kid Hat
$600	66	Davy Crockett Flicker
$600	66	Hagar The Horrible (gold)

VALUE	RANK	RING TYPE
$600	66	Howdy Doody/Poll Parrot T.V. Flicker
$600	66	Joe Penner Face Puzzle
$600	66	Snap, Crackle & Pop (Pop)
$600	66	Spiderman (silver)
$600	66	Tim
$550	76	Shadow Blue Coal
$525	77	Captain Midnight Skelly Oil
$525	77	Captain Midnight Whirlwind Whistle
$500	79	Captain Midnight Initial Printing
$500	79	Captain Video Secret Seal (gold)

VALUE	RANK	RING TYPE
$500	79	Dick Tracy Secret Compartment
$500	79	Gene Autry Eagle
$500	79	Golden Nugget Cave
$500	79	Howie Wing Weather
$500	79	Huskies Club
$500	79	Mickey Mouse Glass Dome
$500	79	Quake Figural (Captain)
$500	79	Range Rider
$500	79	Rootie Kazootie Lucky Spot
$500	79	Roy Rogers Saddle

VALUE	RANK	RING TYPE
$500	79	Secret Agent Lookaround
$500	79	Shirley Temple
$500	79	Snap, Crackle & Pop (Snap)
$500	79	Space Patrol Printing
$450	95	Captain Midnight Flight Commander
$450	95	Captain Midnight Marine Corps
$450	95	Clarabelle Horn
$450	95	Clyde Beatty Lions Head
$450	95	Radio Orphan Annie Silver Star
$450	95	Tennessee Jed Look-Around

Agent 007 Flicker
(set of 12), 1960s $20

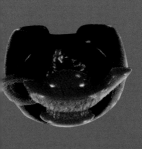

Apollo Flicker
(set of 12), 1960s, $30

Aladdin's Lamp
$30

Arby's Bugs Bunny Flicker
(set of 4), 1987, $40

Andy Pafco's Score Keeping
1949, $200

Arthur Murray Spinner
1976, $200

Baseball Flicker
(set of 10), 1960s, $30

Babe Ruth Muffets
1934, $300

Barnabus from Dark Shadows TV show
1969, $1000

Baseball, New York Mets in package
1970s, $40 (complete in package)

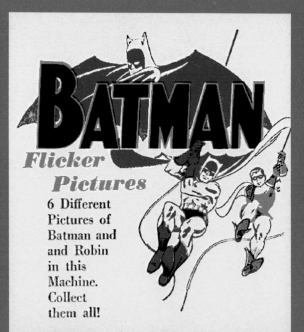

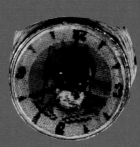

Batman Clock Flicker
1960s, $50

Batman Vending Machine paper for the Batman flicker rings
1966, $35

Batman Flicker
(original silver base)
1966, $25

Batman Figure
1990s, $15

Buck Rogers Birthstone
1934, $400

Bazooka Joe Initial
1940s, $400

Buck Rogers Repeller Ray
1930s, $3000

Beatles Plastic
(set of 4) 1964, $15

Belt Buckle
1950s, $60

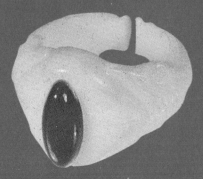

Buck Rogers Ring of Saturn
(glows in dark)
1940s, $850

**Buck Rogers Sylvania
Light Bulb**
1953, $2700

Captain America
1980s, $100

Bullwinkle
1969, $70

Captain Hawks Secret Scarab
1937, $1500

Buster Brown Flicker
1950s, $60

Captain Marvel
1940s, $2500

Captain Midnight Mystic Sun-God
1947, $2100

Captain Video Flying Saucer
1951, $1200 complete

**Captain Midnight
Flight Commander**
1957, $1000

Casper The Friendly Ghost
1950s, $30

Captain Video Seal, copper top
1951, $600

Charlie McCarthy
1940s, $425

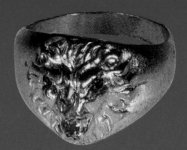

Clyde Beatty Lions Head
1930s, $450

**Cisco Kid Secret
Compartment**
1950s, $7500

Count Chocula Flicker
1980s, $75

Clarabelle Face/Hat
1950s, $1500

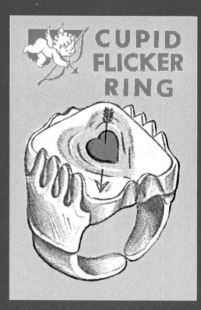

CUPID
FLICKER
RING

Clarabelle Horn
1950s, $450

Cupid Flicker Ring vending machine pape
(Valentine ring), 1960s, $15